BATTLE DRESS

RETURN VIA DUNKIRK

BY
GUN BUSTER

BATTLE DRESS

BY
GUN BUSTER

London: HODDER & STOUGHTON, 1942

First printed	.	.	.	July	1941
Reprinted	.	.	.	August	1941
Reprinted	.	.	.	August	1941
Reprinted	.	.	.	November	1941
Reprinted	.	.	.	February	1942

Made and Printed in Great Britain for Hodder & Stoughton, Limited, London
by Wyman & Sons Limited, London, Reading and Fakenham

CONTENTS

		PAGE
I.	" FRONT LINE "	9
II.	A MEETING WITH DESTINY	31
III.	NOT ACCORDING TO RULES	47
IV.	SIX IN A TRENCH	69
V.	A JOB OF WORK	85
VI.	ONE OF THOSE MYSTERIES	109
VII.	A BRUSH WITH REFUGEES	123
VIII.	THE DUMP AT BETHUNE	141
IX.	AT THE MENIN GATE	163
X.	RACE WON BY DEFAULT	189
XI.	A DUNKIRK DIARY	207
XII.	" BATTLES LONG AGO "	231
XIII.	ACTIVE SERVICE	245

"FRONT LINE"

I.—" Front Line "

Four officers sat chatting on the patch of lawn outside the Officers' Mess at a military depôt in the North of England. Dinner was over and the long June evening would soon fade into night. But low on the horizon a crimson, flaming sunset still lit up the silhouette of the distant manufacturing town with its fiery red glory. The senior officer present, an Infantry Major, seemed fascinated by the spectacle. He could not take his eyes off it.

" There's something terribly familiar to me about that," he observed, nodding his head in the direction of the glowing roof-tops. " What does it remind you of ? "

" Something I've been trying to forget ever since we came out here," said the Infantry subaltern sitting next to him. " Dunkirk has killed my pleasure in ' shepherd's delight ' sunsets for good. I'll never see one again without thinking of Dunkirk promenade ablaze, and myself marching into the furnace."

He gave a slight shudder, and readjusted his chair so that he sat with his back to the flaming horizon.

The four men had only arrived at the depôt thirty-six hours before. They had been among the last few thousands to be evacuated from Dunkirk, and had met for the first time in the Northern barracks to which hundreds of officers and men, bits and pieces from the various units of the B.E.F., found themselves entrained on their debarkation in England. The Major and the subaltern came from different regiments. A Gunner Captain and a Captain in the Tanks completed the little group on the lawn. Except for the latter, all displayed very stained and worn battle-dress, having lost all other kit. The Tank Captain had lost his, too. But his home was not far from the barracks, which enabled him to send over for a fresh outfit. Resplendent in the luxury of new tunic and slacks he presented a dapper contrast to the other three scarecrows. The dilapidation of the Major was increased by a pair of carpet slippers, two sizes too big for him. But he regarded that as a blessing. The sores on his feet, a legacy of the final stages of the Retreat, were giving him hell. When he arrived at the depôt the afternoon before, it had taken him nearly half an hour to peel his socks off, and even then he lost two or three inches of skin. The thought of a pair of boots rendered him positively sick.

" One of these days, I suppose, all will become clear as King's Regs.," he said, still contemplating the blazing sunset. " But at the present moment it beats me how the Germans come to be in Dunkirk, while we're back in England without the change of a shirt until we buy one."

" Simple," said the subaltern emphatically. " Too many assistants. That was our trouble. We'd have done better on our own. At least, we'd have known where we stood. And that's what we never did know over there. More than half the time we weren't fighting at all. Just going back. If we weren't going back because of the French we were going back because of the Belgians. That's how it went on. Allies ! . . .

Heavy liabilities, rather. And when the Belgians defaulted, that broke the bank completely."

"Don't forget their 1914 equipment and horse-drawn transport. What chance had they from the start ? " interposed the Major.

"Perhaps not. . . . Still . . ." said the subaltern, trying to preserve a balance of fairness in the midst of his bitterness. " But the chief point is that whenever it came to a straight fight between us and the Germans, we held them. And that's putting it modestly."

" Oh, I agree. Man to man, the British soldier proved he had nothing to fear by comparison with the German. That's the one cheerful feature in the whole dismal business. I've no doubts on that score, and from my own experience I'll tell you why."

The Major gingerly settled his sore feet on a vacant chair.

"After my battalion withdrew through Menin we were ordered to make a stand on the lower edge of the Messines Ridge. You know the locality, I expect. Mount Kemmel, with the church on top, sticking up behind. In front nothing but flat beet fields with the Lys wandering in the centre. It was night when we arrived, and we dug in on the forward slope. We had a three thousand yards front to hold, and as the battalion had been knocked about a bit on the Escaut we couldn't populate it as densely as I'd have liked. In fact, the line was devilish thin. I sincerely hoped that whatever was going to hit us wouldn't be tanks.

" It wasn't. When morning broke a heavy force of mechanised infantry attacked us. I should think they outnumbered us by about three to one. A lot of desultory firing continued for a few hours all along the line. Except on the left flank, which C-company was holding. Here the fire grew in intensity, and, in addition to machine-guns, the enemy began plastering the position with those heavy trench mortars they sprung on us.''

The Major turned towards the subaltern.

'' By the way,'' he interjected, '' I don't know what impression you gained, but it seemed to me all through that our trench mortars were practically non-existent.''

'' I think I saw one once,'' replied the subaltern, with sarcasm. '' We had bombs without mortars. Other people had mortars without bombs. You were saying just now, Major, that your depleted battalion had to hold a front of three thousand yards. That's nothing. I can tell you a better one than that. Coming over on the boat a Machine Gun fellow gave me his solemn oath that his battalion held a front of seventeen miles on the Lys between Armentieres and Halluin for two days, and when they were eventually relieved it was by a Division ! Fortunately for them the Germans never prodded in that direction during those two days.''

'' Good story—if true,'' commented the Major. '' Anyhow, I was quite content to have to hold three thousand yards. Our Battalion Headquarters was in the cellar of a farmhouse, some three-quarters of a mile behind the front line. Towards noon a runner came in from C-company with a message saying they were being attacked by strong enemy forces endeavouring to force a wedge between C-company on the extreme left flank, and B-company next to it on the right. I sent the runner back with instructions, but he never got through. The firing became heavier than ever on the left, and half an hour later a runner from B-company arrived. They'd tried to get into communication with C-company, but failed. There wasn't any doubt that C-company had been completely cut off and surrounded. I dispatched a reliable sergeant

and two men as a small patrol to see if they could
get through. After a long and anxious wait they
returned. They found it impossible to penetrate the
enemy infantry. C-company was ringed round good
and proper. The outlook for them was black. We
gave them up as lost, and moved our reserve company
forward to counter-attack the enemy break through.

" But the break through never came. At least,
not by the Germans. To the utter amazement of
B-company, they suddenly heard a burst of wild
shouting and cheering, and saw C-company come
charging with fixed bayonets through the Germans
towards their left flank. Still more amazing, the
enemy stopped firing and fled in terror before the
onslaught. Those that didn't run did the ' Kamerad '
business, or else received eight inches of cold steel.
It was so methodical it resembled a bit of bayonet
drill. Only, not with dummies. B-company sergeants, watching it, could scarcely refrain from
shouting : ' In ' . . . ' Out.' . . .

" C-company commander came along later to B.H.Q.
to give the Colonel the details. They had been completely surrounded, but continued returning the
enemy's fire until their ammunition was practically
exhausted. Surrender faced them. But they thought
they'd try a last chance. The Company Commander
held a quick conference with the platoon officers and
some of the N.C.O.'s, and it was decided to try to
fight their way out towards B-company. The order :
' Fix Bayonets ' was given. At the signal of the
Company Commander's whistle they charged. He
told me himself he was never more amazed in his life
than when he saw the Germans bolt. They'd only
tried it on as a forlorn hope, thinking a few might
get through, at the most. Actually, they never had
a single man wounded in the charge. The sight of

the bayonet must have petrified the Germans. They simply stopped firing and ran. Extraordinary, wasn't it ? Now you know why I back the British soldier against twice his size in Germans, despite Dunkirk and all."

*　　*　　*　　*　　*

"Unfortunately," interposed the Tank Captain, "this is not exclusively a war of men. It happens to be a war of machines. The men, however good, can't function properly except through machines. If you want to know what beat us, it was the dive-bombers and tanks. Machines, in fact. The best men, equipped with the best machines, will be the winners of this war. It can't be done in any other way. Machines, machines, machines . . . all the time. The best machines. And floods of them. Then we shall see."

He turned towards the Gunner Captain.

"I consider you fellows were luckiest in that respect," he said. "You trotted out that 25-pounder ' gun-how,' easily the best weapon of its size on either side."

"Which only makes it all the more heartrending that we had to blow the lot up," the Gunner mourned. "Yes, she's a lovely gun."

"What about your own stuff ? " queried the Major. "They were all right, weren't they ? "

"Our tanks were all right. As far as they went. But they didn't go far enough," the Tank Captain replied. "We never expected our light tanks would come up against German 30-tonners. Like a destroyer taking on a battleship. And what a hide they had . . ."

He broke off, sucked in his lips, and continued with a vindictive longing.

"I'd love to lay hands for a few moments on that ' friend of a friend.' "

" Oh ?   Who's he ? " inquired the Major, puzzled.

" The fellow who before the war was touring in Germany in his car and was supposed to have bumped into a German tank and found it was made of papier-maché.   You remember. . . . The story went through the newspapers. . . . ' A friend of mine when touring,' etc. etc. . . . By God !   I wish I could have bumped him up against some of the papier-maché *we* bumped into around Arras. . . .

" However good our tanks were," the Captain continued after a pause, " it couldn't compensate for the fact that there wasn't enough of them.   You've not only got to have a good machine.   You've got to have a lot of it.   Machines on the battlefields are just like men.   They can't go on for ever.   They want rest.   Time for recuperation.   Our chief trouble was that we hadn't enough tanks to enable us to spare the time on maintenance we ought to have done.   They never had a chance of going into dock.   I've seen fellows doing repairs in the middle of an action, and getting killed while doing so.   Repairs that ought by rights to have been done in the shops.   It happened any amount of times.   Listen :

" During the push south-west of Arras I was in command of four tanks.   It was just the time when the enemy launched that heavy counter-attack which eventually drove us back.   We'd already been on the move for six days, and in action twice, without a overhaul.   Late in the afternoon Battalion Headquarters wirelessed that a small force of enemy tanks was reported in the neighbourhood of Beaurains.   Would I go and take care of them.

" We rolled down the road and at the outskirts of the village I gave orders for deployment into some fields on the right.   I was about a hundred yards in front, with a couple of tanks on my right and the

15

other on my left. Between us we covered a front of
over a quarter of a mile. We were ambling along very
comfortably when we suddenly spotted six medium-
sized enemy tanks coming towards us round the edge
of a wood two thousand yards away. We went on
to close with them and opened fire at a thousand
yards. They hadn't waited so long. Already their
shells were bursting all over the fields, mixed up with
machine-gun fire. Then I let them have it with our
two-pounders. It was grand shooting. We stopped
two dead in their tracks, one burst into flames, and
another limped away out of action.

" I continued to advance, and after a while took a
squint through the periscope to see how the others
were faring. Believe me, when I switched it round
to the left I couldn't see any tank at all. I switched
to the right and could only see one, the one nearest
to me. I had to turn the periscope right behind me
before I discovered what had happened. The two
tanks had stopped dead several hundred yards in the
rear. As I watched through the periscope I saw the
turret of the tank on my left open, and a man jump
out on to the body. I guessed they'd struck engine
or track trouble. Did I curse !

" It was engine trouble. The fellow started to
tinker about with it. He'd hardly begun when I saw
him collapse. At the same moment another man
emerged from the turret. He was out to the waist
when he suddenly folded up, and remained still,
hanging half in, half out, of the turret. Both had
been knocked out by machine-gun fire.

" I took a quick look at the tank on my right, the
stationary one. It was in flames. An easy target,
stuck there in the field. The Germans concentrated
all their anti-tank stuff on her. I couldn't see any of
the crew at all. Just smoke and flames. A ghastly sight.

" It was two to two now, and the enemy tanks began to close in. I went forward to meet them when my own engine started missing badly. After a few more shots I had to signal to the remaining tank to withdraw, and as I limped off it covered my retirement.

" We had that action in the bag if it hadn't been for those breakdowns. And they wouldn't have occurred if we'd had the time to devote to proper maintenance. If there's a theme song to this war it ought to be : ' Machines, machines . . . more machines. . . .' Planes, tanks, guns, armoured cars, machine guns, tommy guns . . . all of them."

*   *   *   *   *

" Yes, there's no mystery about that," agreed the subaltern. " What puzzles me is the utter collapse of the French. I can't understand that."

" You're in some damn fine company," chuckled the Major.

" I had a spot of leave in April," continued the subaltern. " I'd just done a spell in the Maginot Line. I came home and told everybody I met what wonderful fellows the French were. Tails up . . . unbeatable . . . and all that sort of thing. And I believed it myself. I blush now to think of it. Who could have guessed they were rotten to the core ? . . . It'll never surprise me now to see them out of the war, like the Belgians. Talk about muddle and inefficiency . . ."

" To say nothing of treachery," added the Major.

" You couldn't distinguish which was which," asserted the subaltern. " They talk about a Fifth Column. It was more like an Army Corps. And that makes me think you can't dismiss this war entirely as a war of machines. I might have thought so myself if I hadn't come back through Ypres. That

17   B

city was simply a big poisonous nest of Fifth Columnists. You couldn't go down a street after dusk without
running the risk of being sniped. They potted at you
from roofs, top-story windows, and even from behind
street corners. Not Germans, mark you, but civilians.
I myself know of three officers who were hit, and any
number of men. From the casualties we might have
been engaged in street fighting. Oh, yes, Ypres was
deadly.

" But, as I say, how much was deliberate treachery,
and how much sheer muddle and inefficiency ? Not
that it made much difference what it was in the long
run. I had a taste of that myself. It may have been
Fifth Column work. It may have been mere crass
blundering. But the result was just as uncomfortable
for us.

" After our battalion withdrew from the Escaut,
my company was ordered to hold up the German
advance in a sector just across the French frontier,
to the south of Halluin. It happened to be part of
the line we had dug on the frontier during the ' sitz.'
You know, Major. The one with all the pill-boxes
looking, as it turned out, the wrong way. But near
the centre of the sector there stood one of those massive
pill-boxes erected by the French Engineers—a great,
rough rectangle of masonry, with a fourteen-feet thick
concrete roof, and steel doors at the back. By luck
this did happen to be facing the right way. I mean
in the direction of the enemy. It was past midnight
when we arrived, and we liked the look of that little
fortress. We carried a couple of anti-tank guns—
that 27-millimetre weapon we adopted from the
French—and could mount them nicely in the pill-
box. And, meanwhile, the fourteen-foot roof afforded
good protection against dive-bombers. As soon as
his eye alighted on it the Company Commander began

18

to evolve a defensive scheme pivoting on this pill-box. It was going to be invaluable.

"But when we tried to get inside we couldn't. The place was entirely deserted. The powerful steel doors were locked tight, like a bank safe. No sign of any keys. We spent some time scouting around the district in the hope of finding some of the French Engineers. But there wasn't a soul to be seen. Not even any French civilians. Everyone had fled. Then we tried to break the doors in. We bashed at them with rifle butts, kicked and shoved, and made football charges, a dozen of our heftiest at a time. All that happened was that more than half the company got bruised shoulders. Those steel doors didn't budge an inch. They'd have been an acquisition to the Bank of England. As it was, we cursed them good and plenty.

"Battalion Headquarters was three-quarters of a mile behind, and eventually the Company Commander despatched a runner on a bicycle to ask if they knew of the whereabouts of the keys. B.H.Q. didn't know any more than we did. They 'phoned through to Brigade. They, too, had never heard of any keys. They made the very helpful suggestion that we should inquire of French troops in the vicinity. There weren't any. We'd already discovered that.

"Meantime, we began to hear distant firing in front of us. Not much at first, but it gradually increased in volume. It was pretty clear that the enemy was pressing forward, trying to force the crossing of the Lys. We had to get a move on. So the Company Commander deployed the troops in trenches and at other points on the line. But he was savage at being unable to make use of the pill-box. It threw his nice little defensive scheme right out. It was pretty rough having a strong point right on your doorstep and being unable to benefit by it.

" ' Get on your motor-cycle,' he said to me, ' and go into M——. See if you can find anyone there who knows anything about the keys. Try the mayor.'

" M—— was the nearest town, about six miles away. As I tore along in the darkness I couldn't help thinking what a strange war this was. I'd never dreamed I should find myself running about on the battlefield in the dead of night hunting for a bunch of keys. Incredible, isn't it ? I found M—— like a grave. All the inhabitants had quitted. But I managed to run the mayor to earth at last. He was hiding in the cellar of a garage ready, I expect, to bolt first thing in the morning. Of course, he hadn't got any key. I asked him if he knew the whereabouts of the French Engineers who had built the pill-box. They'd quitted the district two days ago, he informed me. Just walked out, I concluded, taking the key with them, without caring a damn what might happen.

" On my way back to our sector I ran into a bunch of R.E.s coming up a road from the Lys. And as luck would have it a Sapper friend of mine was in command. We stopped for a bit of a chat, and I told him the tale of the pill-box.

" ' Why so much fuss ? ' he said airily. ' Looking for keys ! . . . Blow the damn thing open.'

" ' We're not like you, a gang of dynamiters,' I replied. ' We don't know how to blow it open. And if we did, we've nothing to blow it open with.'

" ' How far away is this safe ? ' he inquired.

" ' About a couple of miles.'

" ' Well, wait a moment. If you like I'll come along and do the job for you. It'll be a pleasant change. I've been doing nothing but blow up bridge-heads on the Escaut and Lys for days.'

" He went back to the section, collected a few men, and we set off. We'd proceeded about a mile when, to my astonishment, I met the Company withdrawing. The German engineers had run a pontoon across the Lys under cover of darkness, and the instant it began to get light the enemy attacked with tanks and strong forces of infantry. Our Company suffered a lot of casualties and after hanging on for a bit received orders to withdraw.

" ' If we could only have got inside the cursed pill-box we could have shot those tanks to hell,' exclaimed the Company Commander bitterly.

" I introduced him to my Sapper pal, and explained.

" 'Thanks for coming. But it's too late now,' he said. ' Beaten by a bloody key ! '

" Now, if that wasn't Fifth Column business, it strikes me as being something just as bad."

*   *   *   *   *

" Whatever it was, we had a more dangerous unseen enemy to contend with than that," observed the Gunner Captain. " I'm quite ready to admit that dive-bombers, hordes of tanks, Fifth Columnists, treachery in high places, bad Allies, all played a part in the débâcle. But, in my opinion, there was something more important than any of those."

" After that list, there doesn't seem much else left," laughed the Major.

" A powerful psychological factor," continued the Gunner. " Something that was always deep at the back of our minds, however much we thought we'd got rid of it."

" What's the diagnosis, doctor ? " inquired the subaltern, sceptically.

" Front-Line obsession, my youth," said the Gunner. " A complaint inherited from the last war."

The Major, who himself had fought in 1914–1918, sucked at his pipe and looked thoughtful.

" I'd like to hear more about this," he said.

" Did you ever see a Front Line over there, Major ? "
asked the Gunner. " I mean a Front Line as in the
last war, with a support line behind it, and a reserve
line behind that, and then a mile of entrenched country
through which it was almost impossible for a single
enemy to penetrate."

" I should say not. Nor did anyone else. In the
last war you could point to your Front Line and bet
your boots you wouldn't find any enemy till you
reached it. It was rather different this time, I must
say."

" Most of the time there wasn't any Front Line
worth calling the name," said the Gunner. " The
best you could do was to indicate a strip of ground
five miles deep in which fighting was taking place.
In that strip, besides infantry, there would be artillery
units, Sappers, R.A.S.C., Signals, all of which were
likely, at any moment, to have to beat off an attack
at close quarters. And not all of them were equipped
for it. You found batteries attacked from the rear,
and R.A.S.C. columns running up against tanks.
And they had no better means of defending themselves than in the safe old days of 1918. That wouldn't
have been the case if we had really understood all
the implications of mobile warfare and made every
unit a complete little defensive force in itself.

" The odd thing is that everybody knew this was
going to be moving warfare, fought with 'planes and
tanks and armoured vehicles. Everybody talked
mobility. But we didn't practise it enough in the
years before the war owing to lack of equipment.
On manœuvres you saw private cars and tradesmen's
vans with flags sticking up on them, pretending to be
tanks. And batteries that had to leave half their
guns at home because of the shortage in transport

vehicles. That meant that the lessons of mobile
warfare were never fully rubbed in. It also meant
that the old ideas of 1914–1918 were never fully
rubbed out. At the back of all our minds there still
persisted, like an ineradicable weed, the old Front-Line
obsession. You found it cropping up in all sorts of
places. I know a C.O. who couldn't believe his
battalion was in grave danger because the preliminary
enemy shell fire had been so slight. He was still
thinking in terms of the barrages on the Somme and
mass infantry attacks. Meanwhile the damage was
being done by a screen of a dozen motor-cyclists,
half a dozen tanks, and between two and three hundred
motorised infantry, who weren't delivering any frontal
attack, but just seeping in here and there, wherever
they could find an unguarded crack.

" As for the French, they seemed completely
bewildered when they hunted round and couldn't
find a Front Line. Their strategy went to bits
entirely."

" They thought they could win the war by sitting
underground in the Maginot Line, watching the
Germans through a periscope," growled the subaltern.

" The Maginot Line has a lot to answer for," said
the Gunner. " More than anything else, in my
opinion, it helped to perpetuate the insidious disease
of Front Line Obsession. It stood there like an
eternal symbol. There was no chance of forgetting
it. True, the Germans built the Siegfried Line. But
at the same time they contrived to rid their minds
of the old 1914–1918 ideas much more thoroughly
than we did. They beat us there, psychologically.
We went into mobile warfare with an intangible brake
on. They didn't."

" We shan't next time," said the subaltern.

The Gunner Captain remained silent.

" I was thinking," he explained after a pause, " of one battery I know for whom there won't be a ' next time.'

" Just before war broke out we had a second-line regiment formed. The senior officers chiefly consisted of men off the reserve. The young subalterns had no experience at all. They were hurried through as much training as possible in the shortest time.

" Much to our surprise, we discovered in April that they were in France, even before some first-line regiments. Their equipment made us laugh—18-pounder Mark 2 guns that had gone out of fashion early in the last war. In fact, the regiment was a mixture of ancient and modern. Modern battle-dress, modern transport, old weapons.

" Then came the invasion. During the last week of the retreat the regiment eventually found itself in action near Cassel. Unfortunately for them the Germans were pressing very hard in that sector, and already on this particular day the Colonel and the Second-in-Command had been badly wounded by a shell-burst.

" The battery on the left of the sector was in position behind a hedge near the corner of a big field on the side of a sunken road. They were supporting a line of hard-pressed infantry two miles or so in front, carrying out harassing fire tasks and shelling enemy concentration points in the usual orthodox manner. In fact, so far it was war *à la* 1914–1918. They hadn't the slightest suspicions of the rude awakening they were about to get. There they sat, lobbing over their shells in the direction, as they thought, of the enemy— and the front line.

" So it went on till late in the afternoon, when suddenly from their right rear came the rattle of machine-gun fire and a complete gun crew crumpled

24

up, dead and wounded. Another burst of fire followed, and another, and the battery realised it was
being attacked from behind. They couldn't tell how
strong the enemy were, but the firing grew more and
more intense. And in a little while bombs from trench
mortars began exploding in the position. At this
identical moment they spotted five German tanks
bearing down on them a mile or so away.

" There was only one thing to be done in the circumstances, and they did it. The Troop Commanders
shouted orders to swing the guns round to engage the
tanks. It was a right-about-face. Too big a switch
for the traverse. To accomplish it the gunners had
to pick up the trail of the gun and man-handle it
round. A wicked job under close machine-gun fire
all the time. Half the gun crews were shot to bits
in no time. However, they managed to swing the
guns round at last, pointing now in the opposite
direction to what they had regarded all day long as
being their ' front line.' In fact the fire in this
quarter had ceased for some time.

" Meantime, at the Wagon-Lines a mile and a half
behind the battery position, where all the vehicles
and reserve ammunition were parked, no one dreamed
of the disaster that had befallen the battery. So
little, indeed, did they imagine it was in any danger
that the Wagon-Lines Officer said to the Battery
Quartermaster Sergeant :

" ' Just take a trip up to the battery, and see if
there's anything they want.'

" The B.Q.M.S. hopped on his motor cycle and sped
off up the road towards the gun positions. Knowing
all the turns in it he drove along without paying much
attention beyond thinking what a fine afternoon it
was. On drawing nearer to the Battery he heard a
lot of machine-gun fire mixed up with the roar of the

guns. He presumed this to be coming from our own infantry and, without giving it further thought, turned the last bend and ran slap into a detachment of five German infantrymen scouting along the road. They pulled him up and disarmed him. One man was left behind with him as a guard, and the others proceeded down the road in the direction of the Battery position.

" The B.Q.M.S. began to think quickly. It dawned on him that the Battery had been surprised and was in a bad way. Machine-gun and rifle fire echoed incessantly from over the crest of the embankment at the side of the road. Occasionally there sounded the crack of an 18-pounder, but these became less and less frequent as the crews were shot down and the guns put out of action.

" As the minutes passed the guard on the B.Q.M.S. grew more and more excited. He was obviously burning with curiosity to see what was happening over the other side of the embankment. Finally he could resist temptation no longer. He clambered up the embankment and stood looking towards the Battery with his back to his prisoner.

" There was only a distance of four yards between them, but the B.Q.M.S. determined to make a dash for it. He was still sitting astride his machine. Very cautiously he edged it round, praying that the German wouldn't glance over his shoulder. But the fellow was too keen on watching the ' kill ' on the other side of the road to notice anything else. The B.Q.M.S. set the controls, put it in gear, got the clutch in and hoped to God it would start first kick.

" He kicked. There was a splutter . . . a roar . . . and the machine leaped forward. The German spun round, raised his rifle and fired . . . fired again. Both bullets went through the B.Q.M.S.'s leg, but by now he was round the bend and nothing could stop him. Half-fainting from the pain of his wounds he reached the Wagon-Lines and gasped out the tragic news.

"The Wagon-Lines Officer didn't wait to be told twice. He immediately packed up and despatched the column to a rendezvous a few miles back while he drove off to contact R.H.Q. and report the disaster.

"Battery wiped out, I suppose," said the Major after a brief silence.

"Except the few who are now prisoners in Germany," replied the Gunner. "Front Line obsession has to answer for that little affair, as for a lot of others. It's very easy to be wise after the event, and I'm not trying to blame anybody. How can you when it's a matter of a psychological attitude that isn't exactly within one's control. We were all infected, more or less. We know a lot of things a damn sight better now. One is that in this new warfare a battery is always liable to be attacked from the rear, and that it may have to fight by itself without the help of its own infantry. The Front Line is anywhere. And everybody's in it."

* * * * *

"Well, we've held the inquest," said the Major, rising. "In a hundred years we'll have the verdict. It'll be called history. While waiting, I'm going inside to attend to my feet."

A MEETING· WITH DESTINY

II—A Meeting With Destiny

SITTING alone at his table under the camouflaged canvas awning, the Adjutant of the 555th Field Regiment R.A. delivered himself of a deep breath, deep enough for a sigh. He pushed his tin hat a long way off his forehead till a peak of thin, flat, gingerish hair became visible. Damp with sweat, it looked flatter and thinner than ever now. And on his damp forehead the big sandy freckles stood out like walnut stains.

It was nearing seven in the evening, a perspiring end to a long perspiring day. All the palpitating heat generated since dawn seemed to the Adjutant to be concentrated in this gasping hour. Not a breath of air to slake the furnace. The ideal moment, he thought, for a double whisky and splash.

A sad thought. The nearest whisky he could visualise was miles away to the north-east in the regimental mess vehicle. He merely had the comfort of knowing its map reference. The regiment, following up the fast-moving infantry, was travelling light. All the B-échelon vehicles, including, as well as the mess vehicle, most of the stores and general paraphernalia of the regiment, had been left to follow up the quick advance south at a more leisurely pace. If the advance continued at the same pace it might

be days before the B-échelon vehicles—and the whisky
—caught up the regiment.

The Adjutant wasn't quite sure that he approved
of this fast-moving warfare. He was thirty-five years
old, too young to have fought in the last war. But
he had heard all about those R.H.Q.'s—even in dug-
outs—where one could settle down really comfortably
for months at a stretch. Where a man could instal
an easy chair, stick pictures on the walls, even have
a piano sent up (very unofficial, of course) from the
Base. To say nothing of the cases of whisky, always
on tap at the end of a fatiguing day. What a contrast
with his present R.H.Q.—consisting solely of the
Colonel's car, the Signal Officer's vehicle with a wireless
set, and the R.H.Q. office truck, all tucked away near
a pig-sty in the corner of a dirty, untidy farmyard
just outside the village of Marœuil. Expecting to be
on the move again at any moment, they hadn't thought
it worth the trouble to accommodate themselves in
the farmhouse. With the help of a stout stake the
Adjutant rigged up an open-air office for himself by
stretching a canvas awning from the side of the Colonel's
car. Thus sheltered from the blazing sun he had
spent the day compiling the usual returns to Division,
and wading through the mass of stuff Division had
presented to him—most of it, he thought, unnecessary.
All the time a litter of strong young porkers rooted
and grunted around his feet, occasionally nearly
pushing him off his canvas stool. For the last three
hours he had been hearing the dull, distant thud . . .
thud . . . of the regiment's two batteries which were in
action four miles away, supporting the infantry in their
attempt to drive the enemy back south-west of Arras.

The Adjutant loosened another button at the neck
of his battle-dress, drew another deep breath, and
resumed his occupation of getting out operation orders.

He finished just as a Don R. from one of the batteries dashed through the farmyard gate. The despatch rider brought with him two messages. The Adjutant opened one of the forms immediately. The other he did not bother to look at then. It was just the usual Casualty Return form. Every day since the Regiment first landed in France, eight months ago, he had received these Casualty Returns from the batteries. The entry was always : " Nil." Every day for eight months a new form, entry : " Nil," had been prepared, which he had signed and forwarded, according to routine, to Divisional Headquarters, thinking at last that it was a bit of waste of time and paper. He had grown so used in the past eight months to seeing that word " Nil " on the daily form that it became a mechanical habit with him to leave the Casualty Return unopened till he had nothing else to attend to. He did so now, concentrating on the other message.

The battery wanted two thousand H.E. shells urgently. The Adjutant reached for an Army form, indented for the required ammunition to the R.A.S.C. Supply Column, entered on the form the map reference where the stuff was to be delivered, and despatched the Don R. without delay. When the noise of his motor-cycle died away down the road the Adjutant, with nothing else to do at the moment, idly opened the Casualty Return.

For a second or two he stared at the form. Had it contained a long list of names from top to bottom he could not have been more surprised. There was one entry only—on the top line. But to the Adjutant, accustomed for so long to the curt and monotonous " Nil," that one name seemed to fill the sheet.

" The first," he said to himself, reading over again the name and details.

C

He turned towards the office truck and called:
" Jimmie."

The Regimental Orderly Officer emerged and sauntered over to him.

" One of your old battery has been killed, Jimmie,"
the Adjutant informed him.

" Who is it ? "

" Sergeant Barber."

" That's a pity. A great pity," observed the Orderly
Officer with a judicial deliberation. He liked to be
definite and precise about his verdicts on his fellow
men. " Barber was a first-rate Number One. His
Troop will miss him."

" Yes. A pity," the Adjutant agreed formally.

The Orderly Officer seated himself on the edge of
the table and folded his arms.

" Curious thing about Barber," he said reminiscently.
" He had a face like a November fog, and a disposition
like the sun in June. He looked a born grouser.
Everybody thought so at first sight. It was quite a
shock when you discovered he was a cheery guy.
I consider Nature played a dirty trick on him, giving
him that misleading face. Must have caused lots of
people to make mistakes. Odd, wasn't it ? "

" Yes," agreed the Adjutant, again formally. At
the moment he was not much interested in Nature's
dirty tricks, and less in the Orderly Officer's epitaphs.
He shouted across to his clerk in the office truck:

" Have you made out the Casualty Return yet,
sergeant ? "

" No, sir."

" Well, when you do here's something to put on it."

Then the Adjutant once more became fully conscious
of the sweltering heat, and unfastened another button.

*   *   *   *   *

34

Inside the office truck the R.H.Q. clerk, stripped of his blouse, stood reading the form the Adjutant had handed to him. He had a personal interest in the information it contained, for he and Sergeant Barber had been cronies during the long spell in billets at Armentières before the Invasion started.

" Poor old Barber . . ."

The memory of many a dish of steak and chips and onions that he and Sergeant Barber had demolished in the evenings at the little restaurant in the Rue des Quatre-Saisons, where they had the bald, talkative parrot, surged up with a painful vividness. He remembered the evening when the parrot bit Barber's thumb, and the blood froze on it like a red icicle during their walk back to billets, on a night with the temperature twenty-two degrees below freezing point. And here he was now, sitting with his blouse off because it was so blasted hot, and he'd give something to take his trousers off, too. And poor old Barber had packed it up. And he'd been talking to him only the day before during a halt outside Givenchy. And . . .

His next recollection perturbed him. He remembered that he had borrowed five shillings from Barber weeks ago, and had never paid him back. He wished now, from the bottom of his heart, that he had given him the money yesterday. You couldn't tell. Old Barber might have been thinking of that five bob he owed him just when he was killed. It might have been his last thought on this earth. Funny things like that did happen. The office clerk wished and wished he had paid that debt. No good wishing. He'd never be able to pay Barber now. He began to get faintly worried. How could he transmit the money to the dead man's heirs ?

" A nasty knock, too, for Ivy . . ."

Ivy was Barber's wife. The office clerk had never seen her. From little things Barber had told him he concluded that it would take very much more than a sergeant's pension to console her for her loss.

Outside in the farmyard, the Regimental Don R., waiting to take the Casualty Return along with others to Divisional Headquarters, five miles back at Vimy, and anxious to get there in time for a meal with his pals at D.H.Q., played a brief tune on his horn as a gentle reminder of his existence.

The office clerk took a new Casualty Return and sat down to fill it in ready for the Adjutant's signature. In the various columns he inscribed the dead man's name, his rank, his official number. When he came to the last column, devoted to " Nature of Casualty," he wrote more slowly and carefully in his best copperplate handwriting :

" Killed in Action."

*   *   *   *   *

Three cold, bare, official words. Laid with a tombstone finality on the name of Sergeant Barber. Three words that summed up officially the meeting between one man and his destiny.

And this is how they met.

The Battery Column, consisting of twelve 25-pounders, with tractors and ammunition trailers, quickened into fifteen miles an hour as it sped down the slight dip in the dusty pavé road leading to the village of Dainville. It was five in the afternoon, and the sun was as hot and brazen as at midday. The battery was in a hurry. They were going into action immediately. in positions a couple of miles the other side of the village. And, for the first time, they were going into action under fire. At the head of the column rode the

36

battery leader on a motor-cycle, and the twelve tractors, each with ammunition trailer hooked on behind and gun hooked to trailer, stretched for three-quarters of a mile along the road. Between each gun and its pursuing tractor a space of a hundred yards was being maintained, in case the moving column should attract the attention of the German bombers. And this was to be expected, for there was very little cover. The road ran between bare fields in which the young crops showed hardly a foot high above the ploughed earth. Here and there were a few trees and bushes, but hardly enough to break the flat monotony. The khaki and black camouflaged beetle-backed tractors, tugging along their loads, stood out startlingly prominent in the brilliant light.

Within the baking box-like interior of the third tractor of the column five men had squeezed themselves into the four seats behind the driver. It was uncomfortable, but they all wanted to have a front view of the road. So tight a fit it was that the gun-layer sat practically on the knees of two of the gunners, protruding so far forward that whenever the tractor gave a jerk the rim of his tin hat clinked against the back of Sergeant Barber's. The sergeant sat in front beside the driver. After a while he grew tired of the attentions of the gun-layer's battle-bowler.

" Can't you be less affectionate ? " he exclaimed, over his shoulder.

The gun-layer had his retort ready, but it was never uttered. Just then a curve in the road brought them in full view of the village. And for a moment the sight stilled every tongue. Three hundred yards in front the ground they were to traverse was heaving like a sea in a heavy swell. Every now and then a wave of earth rose high in the air and subsided in a cloud of yellow and dirty-grey smoke. Walls of houses were falling flat, and bits of roofs flying through the air. In between the clouds of smoke tongues of red flame shot up with flashes that vanished almost as soon as they appeared. But the most frightening phenomenon of all was the rocking, heaving earth.

A flock of German bombers was dive-bombing Dainville out of existence. What magnified the terror of the spectacle to the men inside the tractor was the fact that they could see but not hear. Every now and again they caught a glimpse of a 'plane at the bottom of its dive, but the noise of their own vehicles drowned every other sound. It was as though the tragedy before their eyes was being enacted in a deathly external silence. Bereft of one co-ordinating sense they seemed to be watching some hideous, irrational nightmare.

The gun-layer first found speech.

" Have we got to go through *that* packet ? " he grumbled.

" You've got no call to worry about that packet," said the sergeant brusquely, without turning his head. " You'd better think about getting your gun on the right line. I don't want any of that Aspelaere funny business again. Mr. Preston blasted me to hell because we were two degrees off the line. All owing to your carelessness."

The sergeant's cold douche had the effect of re-lieving the tension within the tractor. Immediately the men began to find relief in speech, concealing their inner apprehensions behind a screen of facetious remarks.

" What a lovely earthquake. . . ."

" Up she goes again. . . ."

" Don't stop at the traffic lights. . . ."

" I see red and amber. But I don't see no green. . . ."

" I wish I'd joined the Navy. . . ."

The column speeded up to over twenty miles an hour as they entered what, a minute or two before, had been the village street. Their one object now was to get through this shuddering hell in the shortest possible time.

" Step on it, boy ! " the gunners yelled to the driver.

The driver needed no encouragement. The tractor plunged forward, bouncing over the heaps of brick and rubble in the road. The gunners hugged one another to save themselves from being tossed about the vehicle as it rocked and swayed. They could see the gun on the ammunition trailer in front of them swinging from right to left like a great ungainly pendulum, at every second threatening to jump its hook and crash into one of the ruined houses. Behind, their own gun was behaving likewise. The roar of the column as it precipitated itself headlong through the clogged street became louder than ever, drowning the detonations of the bombs more completely. But though within the tractor they still could not hear, they could now smell—a bitter acrid mixture of bomb fumes and burning wood. Here and there dead bodies of British soldiers lay sprawled in the roadway or huddled up against the walls of the houses, and once or twice a crouching figure in battle-dress darted across the road from a burning house to seek fresh cover.

The jokes in the tractor subsided. Now that they found themselves part of this heaving dissolving world, words lost their efficacy to relieve the strain. Split seconds counted now—a matter of life and death —and one thought alone engaged their minds. Would they get through alive ? The tremendous issue of the desperate race held them breathless. Each yard that took them nearer to the exit of the village strengthened

39

hopes they scarcely dared entertain. Their stiff, wooden attitudes betrayed their emotions. Only Sergeant Barber displayed no change. Curved leisurely in his seat, he remained as unperturbed as if he were on his way to the Derby.

Half-way down the village street a bomb exploded a few yards to their right, bringing down a house and hurling a shower of brick and rubble against the tractor. They dived, bumping and swaying, into a thick cloud of dust, their own noise deafening them. Emerging from the pall the driver mechanically made a wild swerve to avoid crushing to death a soldier who staggered, dazed, into the middle of the road.

" Jay-walker," remarked the sergeant with a grin. " And a lucky one."

The dust lifted slightly. So did their fears. The end of the village was in sight. Beyond they could see green fields. By comparison with the hell they had driven through this surely meant safety.

" Good boy. . . . Good boy . . ." the gunners began yelling frantically to the driver. " We've made it. . . . We've made it. . . ."

Suddenly, above their excited shouts, a new noise penetrated the interior of the tractor. A noise unlike anything they had been hearing. A sharp, high-pitched whine. Just the flick of a sound. Here, and gone in a fraction of a second.

For a moment or two no one took any notice. Not even when the figure of the sergeant in front crumpled towards the driver, his head drooping over the steering wheel. The driver, intent only on the road, thought the sergeant was crowding him too closely, and put out a hand to shove the drooping head back. Instantly he snatched it back, covered with something warm and sticky. He shot one horrified glance at the sergeant's face. The shock he received caused him momentarily to lose his head. Unconsciously he endeavoured to escape from the dreadful thing beside him. He violently jabbed his foot on the accelerator and the tractor took a great lurch forward, hurling the men behind into a heap.

The gun-layer, a bombardier, was the first to recover his wits.

" Pull up," he ordered.

The tractor came to a halt by the side of a field, with green shoots of corn just popping through the brown earth. They lifted out the body of Sergeant Barber and laid it on the grass verge by the roadside. Dainville, a smoking, flaming ruin, was still being bombed behind them, and shells from the German artillery were bursting in the fields around. The battery tractors in their rear roared past them without any slackening of speed.

In the glare of the sunshine, with the gunners grouped round him, the bombardier knelt down and unfastened the sergeant's blouse, to feel his heart. It was motionless. The sergeant was dead right enough, and the gunlayer proceeded with the routine for such occasions. From the sergeant's pocket he removed his A.B.64, the soldier's pocket-book, which contains entries of pay, next-of-kin, and will. That must be handed in to Battery Headquarters. He took out his map and marked with a small pencil dot the position, as near as he could identify it, where the sergeant's body would be left. Battery H.Q. would also want to know this. He satisfied himself as to the nature of the fatal wound : " Bomb or shell splinter in the face."

Thus far the proceedings had been carried on in a gloomy silence. Suddenly one of the gunners commenced whimpering, his nerve giving way under the strain.

" It's all up with us. . . . It's all up with us," he
sobbed. " They'll get the lot of us . . . just as they
got the sergeant. We're as good as dead. . . . Not
an earthly. . . . Not an earthly. . . . Run for it,
boys. Run for it."

The gunner was a man nearly fifty years
of age. The bombardier was a young man of
twenty-five. But he rose fully equal to his
new responsibilities. He caught the gunner
roughly by the shoulder and thrust a fist in his
face.

" Shut up," he ordered. " Shut up, I tell you. Or
I'll clock you one."

His savage expression, and his reputation as a
redoubtable boxer, had the desired effect. The elderly
gunner did not cease to whimper. But it was to
himself.

Again the gunlayer knelt beside the sergeant's body.
He cut off one of the two identification discs and
thrust it in his pocket. His job was over now. Nothing
remained but to leave Sergeant Barber's body there
by the roadside.

" Mount . . ." ordered the gunlayer.

The men climbed back into the tractor.

The young bombardier was the last to mount.
Before doing so he walked back to the body and
placed the sergeant's tin hat over his face to keep
off the flies.

In all, the sergeant had been dead about two
minutes by the time the tractor passed out of
sight.

As to the future, well, if he were lucky the R.A.M.C.
might come along that way and bury him by the
roadside with the remaining identification disc around
his neck, having first entered the information from it
in their records, thus :

" Sergeant Barber. . . . Number——. Found
dead by side of road at—— Cause of death, shell
wound in head. Buried, map reference——. Date."

If he were unlucky it would be the Germans who
would come along that road.

It is like that in moving warfare. Dead and wounded
alike. Officers and men. Only, if you are wounded,
before being left, you'll have a first field-dressing
clamped on. Then you sit by the roadside and wait.

More anxiously than did Sergeant Barber. . . .

*   *   *   *   *

A month later, Sergeant Barber's old Troop Commander walked into the Battery Headquarters in a
camp in the North of England, where the remnants
of the battery were being sorted out and collected
together after the Retreat. He carried in his hand a
letter signed " Ivy Barber," and looked worried.

" Here's an unpleasant business, sir," he said to the
Major. " I've just received a letter from Sergeant
Barber's wife asking about her husband. She says
she has heard the Regiment got back from Dunkirk
safely, and can't understand why her husband hasn't
written to her."

" Doesn't she know what happened to him ? "

" Evidently not."

" Poor woman. The Casualty Return must have
got lost in transit from Division to the War Office.
Burned, perhaps, with other papers to prevent them
falling into the hands of the enemy. Or sunk
coming over. What an awkward thing. It'll be
much harder for her, now that the Regiment has
returned. Not having heard from the War Office
she's sure to think he's safe."

" I wrote her a letter of sympathy at the time,"

said the Troop Commander. " Must have been destroyed, too."

" You'll have to write her another," the Major said. " A very nice one.   It'll be difficult."

The Troop Commander found it so difficult that it took him half the afternoon.

NOT ACCORDING TO RULES

The young Gunner subaltern, making his way in the early twilight across a triangular field that approached the summit of a low ridge, thought it a rum go. Not at all warfare as he had imbibed it at Woolwich. Artillery as front-line troops. . . . That'd make the professors screw their eyebrows! He'd give all his field allowance (provided it was a short war!) to watch their expressions could they see his Battery now. It had just pulled into positions by the side of a small wood three-quarters of a mile behind. And as far as they knew there was nothing between them and the advancing enemy. Not so much as a single platoon of the infantry of the Division to protect them from being over-run. A bit of a mess-up. . . . And damned uncomfortable, too.

The Division had been rushed forward to form a defensive line through which were withdrawing the broken remains of a mobile column that had been severely counter-attacked south-west of Arras. The column had been flung into a very fast battle after two days on the march. German 30-ton tanks had crashed through them. Very many of their own tanks were destroyed. Remnants of infantry companies, and bunches of stragglers, dead-beat, dusty, and blear-eyed, had been retreating northwards all day long

through the new defensive positions to escape the
vigorous pursuit of the enemy. According to their
statements the German armoured vehicles and tanks
were advancing so rapidly that an attack might be
expected at any moment. This was serious, for the
supporting Division had been badly delayed by hordes
of refugees. Particularly the infantry. There were
sectors in the line where it seemed very probable that
the Germans would arrive before them.

The sector in front of the Battery the young
subaltern had just quitted, was one of these danger-
spots. Nothing had been seen or heard of the infantry
detailed to support them. Frantic telephoning by the
Battery Commander merely served to confirm his
fears that the infantry were lost. They were supposed
to be on their way to the sector, but Division could
not say where they were at this particular moment.
Doubtless they would arrive in due course. " So would
the enemy," the Major reflected grimly. The last few
stragglers passing through the Battery positions half
an hour ago had sworn that the German advanced
units could not be more than two miles off. The Major,
taking into consideration their agitation, trebled the
estimate. But that brought him small comfort. In
an hour or two night would fall. A nice prospect !
They stood a good chance of losing all their guns.
Well, R.H.Q. had just telephoned they were to stick
there. . . .

Similar uneasy thoughts engaged the mind of the
young subaltern as he began to mount to the top of
the rise. He was reconnoitring a forward Observation
Post from which to direct his battery fire. The warm,
close evening possessed a brooding mystery not much
to his liking just then. Far away on the left he could
hear some desultory shell-fire, very distant and very
occasional. But in front of him the silence remained

unbroken. He drew no encouragement from this. For all he knew he might be walking straight into the arms of the enemy.

He crept cautiously up the last few feet of the ridge and peered over the top. To his great surprise, and relief, he found he had company. On the forward slope a Machine Gun subaltern, in command of a platoon of four Vickers machine-guns, was just digging-in. He was a sturdy youth of about twenty-four, with blue eyes and an engagingly frank countenance.

" Hullo," he greeted the new arrival with a grin. " Seen any infantry about ? "

" Seen any enemy ? " the Gunner replied.

" Not yet."

" Let's hope they've lost *their* way."

" Where are you ? "

" Our first Troop is about three-quarters of a mile behind. Praying for the infantry to arrive. Last the Battery heard was that they'd been seen at some cross-roads or other. Looks as if they've taken the wrong turning. What are your orders ? "

" To stick here."

" Same as ours. Nice mess-up, isn't it ? We stand a fine chance of being over-run. Of course, it won't be so bad for you. You could get out. The Battery couldn't. The Major *is* pleased, I can tell you. Well, I'll just have a scout round Suicide Corner."

After a quick investigation the Gunner subaltern decided that the best and only spot for an O.P. was the little hollow below the crest of the slope that the Machine Gun officer had appropriated for his head-quarters.

" Do you mind if I share it ? " he asked.

" All right," agreed the other. " Be careful, though.

I don't want a whole crowd up here to give it away.
I'd prefer you only had your telephonist."

" We'll keep the party small and select," the Gunner
nodded.   " I'm going to have a snack before any
unwelcome guests arrive.   Have something with me.
It may be our last chance.   Even our last meal.
Curse it ! "

They sat down to a quick meal off bully beef, ration
biscuits, and chocolate, washed down with a bottle
of red wine.   Then the Gunner commenced a silent
registration of the zone in front of him before it grew
too dark.   He studied the features of the landscape
attentively, noting likely points of enemy concentration and approach for armoured vehicles.   He measured
with a protractor on his map their switch, range, and
angle of sight.   The Machine-Gun officer occupied
himself working out harassing fire tasks, the Vickers,
unlike the Bren gun, being capable of fire at indirect
targets.   He made a careful registration of small woods
and pieces of road in the middle distance that he could
bring under fire, if necessary, even in the dark.

By this time a telephone wire connected the O.P.
to the Troop Command Post, with a link to the
Battery Command Post.

" Through by line, sir," announced the telephonist,
testing it.

" Get the Major," said the Gunner. . . . " That
you, Major ? . . . I've got an O.P. . . . Not a bad
one. . . . I've done as much as I can.   It's getting
rather dark now. . . . What I'm interested in is, have
you any information about the enemy ?   There's not
a smell of our infantry in front.   It doesn't look too
rosy.   I'm with a Machine-Gun wallah up here. . . .
Yes.   Four Vickers dug in on the forward slope. . . .
No, he doesn't know anything.   Except that he's been
told to hang on here. . . ."

"So have we," came the Major's voice. "We've got to dig our toes in. Let's hope the infantry show up before dark. If not they'll have an awful job finding their way. I'm still awaiting information from R.H.Q. In the meantime we must be prepared to meet an attack. I'm keeping the tractors close to the gun positions in case we have to pull out hurriedly. I'll send up to you all the spare men I can, with rifles. I think I can let you have a Bren gun or two, and an anti-tank rifle. With those you and your machine-gun friend ought to be able to make a fight of it. In fact, you've got to. Don't forget—directly you spot the enemy let me know."

"Trust me, Major. I won't make any secret of it," replied the O.P. officer ironically.

"Any news?" asked the Machine-Gun officer eagerly, when he had finished.

"Yes. Our troubles are over. The Major is sending up large reinforcements immediately. A dozen gunners armed with rifles that they haven't fired for months. Enough to hold off the whole blooming German army. Oh, yes. He also hopes we shall have a good night."

"P'raps we were wise to have had that meal," said the Machine-Gun officer thoughtfully.

"It was the cleverest thing you or I have done this war," the Gunner observed, with grim conviction.

However, he proved wrong in his figures. Not a dozen, but thirty gunners, led by a sergeant, trailed the telephone line from the Battery up to the O.P. in the gathering dusk. With ten spare machine-gunners this constituted a little force of forty improvised infantry to defend the slope. The two officers spread them out in threes and fours a score of yards down the slope where a slight wave in the ground afforded useful cover. Lying flat in their ditch the gunners told each other what they thought about it.

" Blimey, what a go ! I only joined the gunners
to get out of the infantry, and here I am—P.B.I. . . ."

" Hope there isn't a bayonet charge. . . ."

" You got nothing to be afraid of. Jerries don't
work the bayonet. They use flame-throwers. . . ."

" Remember, boys. Don't shoot till you see the
whites of their eyes, as my old Dad used to say. . . ."

" Your old Dad ! That was Nelson said that . . ."

" Wellington, you mean . . ."

" I mean Nelson . . ."

" At Waterloo, I suppose ? . . ."

The argument terminated in a sharp order from the
sergeant for absolute silence.

It was getting late in the evening now. Not much
light remained. Eastward the night had already
fallen. But in the direction of the south-west it was
still possible to discern dimly the contours of the
landscape. Squatting in the O.P. the two officers
awaited developments with eyes and ears strained.
Long minutes passed. Everything was silent. Even
the distant shelling had died down. The light faded
more and more. A sense of utter isolation grew on
them.

" Bit eerie, isn't it ? " the Gunner remarked to his
companion. " You know, if they are coming at all I
wish to God they'd come now before it gets completely
dark. It won't be so bad afterwards, if we can get
one look at them. Not so thunderingly mysterious."

Barely had he finished when away on the left of the
slope sounded the rattle of machine-gun fire. The
Machine-Gun officer leaped to his feet.

" That's my left section," he exclaimed. " Something's happening. Can you see anything ? "

Both strained their eyes, but from where they stood
could see nothing. A runner panted up. A detachment of German motor cyclists had been detected on

a bit of road a mile and a quarter away. He pointed in the direction.

"Now we start . . ." said the Gunner, solemnly. He studied his map and made a few rapid calculations, snapping out orders to the telephonist hanging on the end of the wire.

"Take Post . . . Fresh Target . . ."

"Through, sir. . . . Through, sir . . ." announced the telephonist automatically, as he transmitted each order.

"Two degrees left of zero lines . . . angle of sight, 20 minutes elevation . . . 3,000 . . . one round gun fire . . ."

The Machine-Gun officer despatched messages by an orderly to his sections.

"Engage when sighted. Be economical with ammunition."

Sharp bursts of machine-gun fire began to echo along the slope, followed shortly afterwards by the roar of the 25-pounders as the Battery came into action.

For a time no reply emanated from the direction of the enemy. Only a white " success " rocket soared up into the sky to inform their H.Q. that they had reached an objective. The artillery and machine-gun fire that greeted their appearance on the road seemed to have surprised them. Darkness was falling so rapidly that they had no means of knowing the strength of the opposition confronting them. Now onwards, it would be necessary to move with caution. So instead of crashing forward with their tanks, they halted while they brought up and de-bussed their mechanised infantry. Just sufficient light was left for the two officers on the slope to distinguish small detachments of German infantry cautiously feeling their way towards the foot of the slope.

" What wouldn't I give now for a couple of companies

of the disappearing Blankshires," the Gunner groaned. " It's damned hard luck on our little lot down there. I wonder where the hell that infantry is."

The Machine-Gun officer, whose mind was of a severely practical cast, did not bother to reply. He saw no point in useless speculations. The infantry hadn't arrived, and the Germans had. That was all there was to it.

The short staccato bursts of machine-gun fire now became frequent. In face of them the advancing enemy hesitated, and sought cover. Their own machine-guns opened fire. Red flashes stabbed the darkness a mile in front of the slope. Bullets whined round the ears of the defenders, and slapped themselves into the ground. Along the ditch the gunners fired straggling volleys, the crack of their rifles filling in the pauses between the machine-gun bursts. A detachment of the enemy rose from the ground and darted forward to another bit of cover twenty yards nearer. They appeared not much more distinct than crouching, moving shadows. A burst of machine-gun fire caught them and half a dozen of the moving shadows moved no more. After that, night swallowed up everything. There was nothing more to be seen.

" I'll send down some harassing fire tasks," said the Gunner officer.

He 'phoned up the Battery Command Post Officer and gave him three or four targets and their map references, all likely points of enemy concentration that he had noted when making his silent registration, especially the copse where armoured vehicles might be concealed.

" Let me know when the Battery starts to fire," he said.

A bombardier who had crawled up the slope from

the ditch suddenly appeared out of the blackness at his elbow.

" Two men hit, sir," he announced. " Gunner Perkins and Gunner White."

" Badly ? "

" No, sir. Flesh wounds in arm and leg."

" Can they walk ? "

" I should think so, sir."

" Well, clap a field dressing on them and send them back to the Battery. They can find their way if they keep touch with the telephone wire. But they'll have to go alone. I can't spare a man."

The bombardier disappeared.

" Couldn't be blacker, could it ? " observed the Gunner subaltern. " I mean the night," he hastened to add.

There was no moon, and only a few stars high in the dark sky. Night had drawn the veil completely round them. Since the fall of utter darkness their machine-guns had preserved silence. Each gunner kept a finger on the trigger, straining his eyes for the slightest sign of movement in the gloom before him. It was one of those black nights when bushes seem to walk. As time passed, and the suspense of waiting grew greater, it was difficult to resist the temptation to open fire on them. Occasionally, from the ditch, a rifle did crack. When that happened it was usually answered from the hidden enemy by a spasm of machine-gun fire.

" Those flashes look a bit closer," said the Machine-Gun officer after one of these spurts.

" I thought so, too," his companion agreed. " They're working nearer. It's about an hour, isn't it, since we saw the last movement."

" Yes. Time we found out what's going on."

Popping a cartridge in his Very Light pistol, the

Machine-Gun officer pointed it at the sky and pulled the trigger. In a second or two the whole area in front was bathed in an artificial moonlight.

"There they are. See them?"

Half a dozen small groups of the German infantry were caught in the bright light, moving cautiously across a broad field nearly three-quarters of a mile away. The four machine-guns on the slope poured volley after volley into them until, after about half a minute, the Very Light expired and the scene was again blanketed in darkness.

"That'll cool their ardour a bit," exclaimed the Machine-Gun officer, highly satisfied.

"You noticed they're at least a quarter of a mile nearer," said the Gunner thoughtfully. "And God knows how long we've got to stay here before that blasted infantry comes, if they come at all. I wonder we haven't been over-run by now. They must think there's a whole blooming Division up here, to be so cautious. That's a consolation, anyhow. But how long will they be deceived?"

"Two hours ought to see us through, at the most."

"Or an hour and a half. Or an hour. . . . We don't know anything, old boy. Except that we're in a very big plate of soup."

Behind them the Battery continued to fire frequently, but intermittently, on the tasks sent down from the O.P. In front the Germans were engaging in a perfect orgy of machine-gun fire, angered at being caught in the Very Light. Bullets whined incessantly over the slope. The distant darkness was alive with red flashes. It gave some satisfaction to the little band on the slope to note that the flashes drew no nearer.

An anxious quarter of an hour passed without any new development. The German firing died down to an occasional spasmodic burst. To the two officers

56

with their eyes fixed steadily in the one direction, the
darkness seemed to grow even more impenetrable and
full of menace. The Machine-Gun officer, practical-
minded though he was, began to be uneasily impressed
by the crowding mystery of it all.

" See if your people have heard anything about that
infantry," he suggested.

The Gunner got through to the Battery Command
Post. " That you, Major ? . . . Any news of the
infantry ? . . . The enemy are pressing us, and it's
difficult to say how long we can hold out. . . . They're
within about three-quarters of a mile . . . in strong
force. . . . I think it's an armoured column . . . there
was the usual screen of motor-cyclists. . . . I couldn't
see any of the vehicles. . . . Too dark. . . . They've
de-bussed infantry, and it's feeling its way forward.
. . . We've caught them once or twice. . . . Don't
know how long it can last, though. . . ."

" I've no information about the infantry," came
the Major's reply. " They seem completely lost.
Keep in touch and let me . . ."

A sudden disturbance at the other end of the wire
caused him to break off. " Hullo ! . . . What's that ?
. . . What's the matter—— ? " he asked.

No answer came. Frantic with fears that the
enemy had broken through, he continued yelling
down the 'phone. After several seconds a strange
voice replied :

" This is the Machine-Gun officer speaking. I'm
sorry to say your O.P. officer has just been hit."

The Major's first thoughts were : " Thank God, it's
no worse. . . ." His first words were : " Hurt
much ? "

" I don't think so, sir. . . . Bullet in the shoulder.
. . . He's just coming-too after a faint. . . . I'll get
him down to you as quickly as I can."

" Yes. Do. I'll send someone else up."

" You needn't do that," interposed the Machine-Gun officer cheerfully. " If you like I can carry on observing here myself. I know all the targets and I have his record by me. It will be rather a waste of time sending up somebody who hasn't seen the zone in daylight."

" That's very good of you. Are you sure you can ? "

" Confident."

" All right. Don't forget to keep in constant touch with me. And when I do hear anything about the infantry I'll let you know at once."

" It can't be too soon for me, sir," laughed the Machine-Gun officer.

The wounded Gunner subaltern was seated, rather limp, with his back against the slope. As gently as possible in the darkness, the Machine-Gun officer removed his companion's right arm from its sleeve and cut away the shirt. He felt lightly with his fingers for the wound, and having affixed a field dressing, bound it tightly up.

" Now you're all right," he said. " Can you walk ? "

" Think so," murmured the wounded man, rising unsteadily to his feet.

" I'd better send a gunner along with you, in case you throw another faint," said the Machine-Gun after a moment's consideration.

While they awaited the arrival of the escort the Machine-Gun officer seemed to have something weighty on his mind. Finally he produced an envelope with an address on it.

" I'd be awfully obliged if you'd do me a favour," he began, diffidently. " You'll be going home soon. When you're fit, d'you mind calling on that address ?

It's a girl I know. . . . She might be interested in an account of how . . . Well, you know. . . . What it was like up here. . . . It has been a bit exciting, hasn't it ? ''

The Gunner subaltern hardly heard. The twinges of pain in his shoulder were atrocious. but he managed to force a nod. With his left arm looping a gunner's neck he disappeared over the top of the slope.

" Good-bye ! Remember me to England," cried the Machine-Gun officer.

He turned, and once again stared into the blackness concealing the enemy infantry.

" Lucky devil," he muttered.

*   *   *   *   *

It was long past midnight. In the farmhouse cellar that was the Battery Command Post the murky rays from a hurricane lamp illuminated the face of a very worried Major. No infantry had arrived, and no news of their whereabouts. On the slope three-quarters of a mile away, the Machine-Gun officer and his little force still held out, but every moment the Major expected a telephone message to say that it was all over. No disguising the fact that the position was critical. Even if they lasted for another couple of hours or so, dawn would soon enlighten the enemy as to the true state of affairs. It looked as though nothing short of a miracle could save his guns then.

On the floor of the cellar, wrapped in their great-coats, the Assistant Command Post Officer, a spare telephonist, and two of the survey staff, lay like logs, in a profound slumber. Opposite the Major at the table sat the Command Post Officer, with a face that reflected the anxiety on his own. Every ten minutes or so the silence in the cellar was broken by the buzz of the service telephone. The operator picked up the receiver, listened a moment, and said : "Line O.K." It was the routine check-up, and the Major, anxiously hoping every time for a message from R.H.Q. announcing the arrival of the infantry, found the continual disappointments making him bad-tempered. The operator's monotonous : "Line O.K." got on his nerves. There was so damn much about that wasn't O.K.

"This touch-and-go business can be overdone," he exclaimed impatiently to the Command Post Officer. "If we don't get orders soon to pull-out, we're finished. I've given up any hope of that bloody infantry."

He mounted the stone steps from the cellar and stood in the doorway, gazing into the darkness towards the distant slope where the machine-gun officer was installed. Suddenly a Very light went up in that direction, followed by machine-gun fire that died down in half a minute. The Major remained for a while, wondering whether the outburst meant a fresh feel forward by the enemy, and how near they were now. Then he was called to the 'phone.

It was the Machine-Gun officer. "Any news, sir ? " he asked hopefully.

"None."

"Oh ! " The drop in his voice could not be mis-taken.

"How are you getting on ? "

"Four men wounded. One gun has jammed. I can't get it going. Worst of all, ammunition 's getting low."

"I'll see if I can get hold of any for you. Keep in touch."

"I will."

There was nothing more of any use to be said. The Major put down the 'phone.

"I'd hate to see anything happen to that boy up there," he said to the C.P.O.

* * * * *

Two a.m. It was time for the A.C.P.O. to relieve the Command Post Officer. His servant shook him out of his heavy slumber and saw that his hand closed safely round the mug of hot, strong tea.

"We're still here, are we?" the A.C P.O. exclaimed, sleepily getting his bearings. "Anything fresh, Major? Is the machine-gun lad still operating?"

"He's doing a grand job," replied the Major. "I only hope it won't be wasted."

"That means the infantry haven't arrived, I suppose. I was hoping they'd take advantage to steal in on my slumbers. Looks as though I've woke up in time for the grand finale."

As the A.C.P.O. sipped his hot tea, and thought how comforting it was, he was seized with compunction.

"I think I'll take our machine-gun pal a present," he said. "He deserves it. A nice flask of hot tea. You don't mind carrying on for a bit?" he asked the C.P.O. "I won't be away long."

In a few minutes he was on his way to the slope, threading the slack telephone wire through his hand for guidance. As he drew near the crest he began to whistle "Rule Britannia" quite audibly to prevent himself being fired on.

The Machine-Gun officer welcomed him as only a man can who is weary of loneliness and longing for someone to have a chat with. The A.C.P.O. thought there was something quite pathetic in his unconcealed delight at receiving a visitor. They squatted in the little O.P. drinking tea, and the Machine-Gun officer talked and talked and talked. It was some time before the A.C.P.O. realised that he was finding relief in this volubility from the strain he had undergone. Then he let him talk on without interruption. " He's dreading the moment when I have to go," reflected the A.C.P.O. And feeling sorry for him, he delayed his departure for twenty minutes.

" I really must get back now," he said at length. " The C.P.O. wants to go to sleep. Are you sure you're all right ? Would you like me to send some-one up ? "

The Machine-Gun officer seemed to be fighting a little battle with himself. But there was only a second or two's pause before he replied quite cheerfully :

" No, thanks. There's not much point in it. I can do all there is to be done. Good-bye . . . It was very good of you to bring that tea up. Just what I wanted."

When the A.C.P.O. was half-way back to the Battery, another Very light went up from the slope, and another burst of machine-gun fire echoed through the dark night.

The Major stood in the doorway of the cellar, awaiting him.

" What's the situation ? " he asked, anxiously.

" There isn't one," replied the A.C.P.O. seriously. " There's just the approaching end. One determined push by the enemy and they'll be through. It may come at any moment. I offered to send someone else up to the O.P., but he wouldn't hear of it. Said he could do all there was to be done. I'm afraid he's right. We'll have a job getting away from here, Major."

The Major cursed unrestrainedly. " Get me the Adjutant on the 'phone," he shouted.

" Any news of that bloody infantry ? " he demanded, as soon as he was through to R.H.Q.

" No," came the reply. " Oh, hold on. . . . Here's the C.O. . . . He wants a word with you."

" What's the position ? " asked the Colonel.

" Getting desperate," said the Major abruptly. " We look like losing the Battery. From now on it's a sheer gamble."

" Hang on. There's a guide out looking for the infantry. They've been found about three miles away. They shouldn't be long now. I hear you have a new officer at the O.P."

" How did you know ? "

" I had a word with Richards here while the doctor was attending to his shoulder before he went to the Casualty Clearing Station. A Machine-Gun officer, isn't he ? "

" Yes," said the Major. " And if ever a man deserved a gong (medal) he does after this little show."

During the conversation another sustained burst of machine-gun fire sounded from the slope, and when the Major had finished with R.H.Q. he found that the Machine-Gun officer had sent down a message to say that he couldn't hold out for more than half an hour.

" That won't do ! " he exclaimed. " Not long enough to give us a chance. We must have another hour. Get through to the O.P."

He gave the Machine-Gun officer the information about the infantry he had received from the Colonel.

" They may be here in half an hour," he said, " but we want another half to be on the safe side. What's your position ? "

" Ammunition running out. Enemy have crept up

63

to within half a mile," replied the Machine-Gun officer briefly.

"For God's sake hold them there."

"I'll have a good try. Can't promise more."

"Keep in touch, and let me know what's happening."

"I will."

But it was some time before the Battery Command Post were to hear from him again. For over half an hour the wire remained completely dead. In the Command Post the suspense became intolerable. Continually the operator tried to connect with the O.P., but there was no reply. There had been no machine-gun fire from the slope, also, for some time. The only sound that broke the silence was the intermittent roar of the Battery's own guns. It was still dark, but as the Major stood in the doorway of the cellar anxiously gazing out into the night, it seemed to him that the darkness was thinning. Most of all he dreaded the coming of daylight. If only the damned infantry would show up. . . . Perhaps, even now it was too late. He imagined the little force on the slope already overrun and the enemy cautiously closing in on the Battery in the darkness. He could stand the torturing silence no longer. He re-entered the cellar.

"I must know what's happened," he said to the A.C.P.O. "You'd better go up to the O.P. and find out. Be careful, in case they're through."

The A.C.P.O. was on the point of leaving the cellar when the buzzer of the telephone to the O.P. came, surprisingly, to life. The Major grabbed the receiver. It was a heavenly relief to hear the Machine-Gun officer's voice, still cheery, though sounding thin and tired.

"I couldn't get through to you, sir," he said.

" The line was broken just by our 'phone, and we've only just discovered it."

" What's the position ? "

" Ammunition practically gone. I don't think 1 can stop the next push. Not seen any infantry, I suppose ? "

" No . . ."

The Major broke off. Outside the cellar there sounded the heavy tramp of marching feet. Almost immediately the figure of an infantry captain loomed in the doorway.

" Yes . . . By God, they're here," the Major yelled down the telephone without restraint. " Just arrived. They'll be up there in no time."

The A.C.P.O. acted as guide to the infantry. Just as he and the infantry captain were approaching the little headquarters on the slope another Very light went up, followed by a brief rattle of machine-gun fire.

" Thank goodness you've come," the Machine-Gun officer greeted them. " That was my last round. I thought I'd make them a farewell present of it."

In a short while a company of the Blankshires were taking up positions and mounting anti-tank guns on the line along the slope that the gallant little force had held intact throughout the dark perilous hours. The Machine-Gun officer felt a load of responsibility drop from his shoulders. It was no longer his show now. And he wasn't sorry.

The 'phone in his headquarters buzzed. It was the Major to inform him that the Battery had been requested to relay a message from M.G. Battalion Headquarters. They were sending up a reserve platoon to relieve him at once.

" Look in at the Command Post as you pass," said the Major. " You've done damn well. And I'd like to tell you so."

But the Machine-Gun officer was thinking of other things as he wearily descended the slope towards the Battery position just before dawn broke. He was thinking of the envelope he had given to the wounded Gunner subaltern a few hours earlier. It was too late to recall it now. But he dearly wished he could. Things had turned out very different for him from the way he had expected when he entrusted the Gunner subaltern with his mission. She wouldn't understand that. It made him go hot all over to think about it.

He hoped she would not jump to the conclusion that he had merely been trying to impress her.

SIX IN A TRENCH

"THAT blasted gun again!" exclaimed the Gun Position Officer with fervour. "Why won't they keep it quiet?"

The young subaltern who was B-Troop Leader, and who was now engaged in changing his shirt, regarded him with an amused grin. The G.P.O.'s smouldering animosity towards Ack-Ack guns in general was a byword in the Battery. And his sharpest hatred concentrated itself on the Bofors.

"Don't be harsh, old boy," said the Troop Leader. "That's a hard-working little gun. It's doing a job."

The G.P.O. snorted. "Job!" he retorted, scornfully, "job!... Don't they know that 'plane is three thousand feet out of range? They'll never hit it in a million years. I don't mind a damn about that. But they'll fool about till they give away our position."

"Might drop a few thousand feet lower and like the look of us if it weren't for the Bofors," the Troop Leader remonstrated mildly.

The pair stood outside the cellar of the farmhouse that was the Troop Command Post. The night before, the battery had pulled into positions just under the Lens side of Vimy Ridge, the steep side. The sharp, wooded slope, with gashes of white chalk intervening between the green tree clumps climbed

69

up in front of them to the cloudless blue of a beautiful noon-day sky, against which the colossal architecture of the Canadian War Memorial on top of the Ridge was silhouetted with an impressive serenity. But so far as concerned the G.P.O. and his companion, the massive reminder of the heroism and self-sacrifice of the men who twenty-two years before had stood in their shoes, who had struggled and fought and died in their thousands to conquer and hold this selfsame consecrated hump of foreign soil, might just as well not have existed. Their attention was entirely focussed on the immediate reminders of their own brand new war. Though they looked towards the memorial they saw it not, for all its mammoth size and emotional significance. All they had eyes for was the tiny German reconnaissance plane, high over-head, humming like a dragon-fly in the blue sky.

" Look. What did I tell you ? " the G.P.O. said.

The Bofors were barking away. Pom-pom-pom-pom-pom . . . Pom-pom-pom-pom-pom. . . . The characteristic rhythm that always aroused the G.P.O.'s worst suspicions. Little white cotton-wool tufts floated high in the sky as the shells burst—all of them well beneath the target.

" Three thousand feet short, if an inch," the G.P.O. calculated contemptuously. . . . " Hell on earth, what's happening now ? . . ."

Caught up in the excitement, the Bren gunners attached to the ack-ack unit under the Ridge had also opened fire. One out of every four bullets they despatched was a tracer. These sped through the air, glowing like bright cigarette ends with wisps of smoke behind them. Tracer bullets help to give the gunner an idea where his burst of fire is going. They can also set fire to a 'plane—if they hit it. But at the present moment any expectation of such an

70

occurrence was as remote from the G.P.O.'s thoughts as it was, indeed, from the realms of possibility. One fact only concerned him ; that even in the sunlight that stream of bright cigarette ends was alarmingly visible. He flung up his hands.

" I give it up," he said in mock despair. " Let's go inside."

The Troop Leader dived after him into the cellar, more amused than ever at his obsession. But it had some measure of justification. The war had been on long enough for artillery—and infantry—to learn that there was precious little sense in giving away your position by opening fire on an enemy 'plane, even if it were within range, so long as it did not attack you. Also, on the way south to Vimy from Flanders the G.P.O. had run up against a friend in another artillery regiment, one of whose batteries outside Brussels had received a direct hit in a dive-bombing attack.

" I'll swear they'd never have found us if it hadn't been for some damned ack-ack guns in the next field," the G.P.O.'s friend insisted vehemently. And the G.P.O. believed him, though it was very likely quite untrue.

So it can be understood that the G.P.O. was by no means joyful when he discovered, installed in the appointed battery area under the Ridge, four Bofor gun emplacements, one of which happened to be only a few hundred yards from B-Troop gun position in the outhouse of a farm. The events of the morning had not tended to soothe him either. On four occasions massed formations of huge twin-engine German bombers had come roaring over the crest of the Ridge, with awe-inspiring fixity of purpose, on their way to bomb Lens, Seclin, and Henin-Lietard. Great mushroom growths of dirty yellow and grey smoke, sprouting into the blue sky and remaining there, announced

in due course the fulfilment of their deadly mission.
Then the bombers flew back the way they had come.
And the Bofors let off at them, just as they had let
off when they went over. And the puffs of their
bursting shells were always so depressingly far behind
the tails of the disappearing 'planes that the G.P.O.,
as well as getting annoyed at what he considered the
dangerous futility of the display, wondered why on
earth somebody didn't make all ack-ack gunners take
a course in duck-shooting.

Then, in addition, three reconnaissance 'planes
hovered over their positions at intervals during the
morning. Which the G.P.O. regarded as likely to
prove a more serious matter. By a stroke of luck,
each time the 'planes were overhead the battery
happened to be awaiting new fire orders. So they
couldn't have betrayed themselves by their own gun
flashes. Real good fortune, that. And those confounded Bofors had probably spoilt it by blazing
away all the time. The G.P.O. condemned it as
positively sinful.

There was one of these lulls in the firing now. In
the gun-pits of B-Troop the gun crews were taking
an " easy," hoping it would last long enough to give
them a chance of a quiet meal. In the barn of the
farmhouse at the rear the cooks were busy boiling
up dixies of tea on the portable petrol cookers, and
frying " cutlets "—thick slices of bully beef dipped
in flour. The appetising smell was wafted through
the open door of the barn. A good cook can do
wonders with bully beef, " cottage pie " being one of
them. A few minutes later a welcome procession of
dixies wended its way towards the gun-pits. The
gunners filled their mess-tins with tea, cutlets and
bread and cheese, squatted on the gun trail or propped
up the side of the gun-pits, and felt at peace with the

sunny world. Glad of a breather from the cellar where he had been working out the S O S lines sent down from the Battery Command Post, the G.P.O. sauntered round checking up ammunition supplies and pouncing with eagle eye on weaknesses in the construction of the pits.

" That wall wouldn't keep out a tennis ball, let alone a bomb splinter. It'd sail right through. Pack it harder, and make it thicker."

" Yes, sir," said the lean-faced sergeant dutifully. He, too, knew all about the G.P.O.'s obsession. He summed it up as " dive-bombing on the brain."

The G.P.O. strolled back towards the Command Post in the cellar, in good trim for his own tea and cutlets. On the way he encountered his Troop Commander, just relieved from O.P. duty, who had walked over to see how the Troop was getting along. The G.P.O. commenced to recite the morning's events, when it dawned on him the Troop Commander was listening to something else. He stopped speaking, and heard it himself—the peculiar high-pitched inter-mittent note of German 'planes coming towards them, with growing intensity, from over the Ridge.

Next second they broke into view—nine twin-engined Stukas, flying over ten thousand feet up, bunched close together in the shape of an arrow-head.

Hardly had they topped the Ridge when the point of the arrow-head seemed to wobble violently. The Troop Commander understood the grim significance of that wobble. At the leader's signal the Stukas circled round the battery area, taking up positions behind one another.

" It's for us this time," the Troop Commander said softly to the G.P.O. Then, at the top of his voice, he roared : " Take cover . . ."

Out of the gun-pit that the G.P.O. had just quitted

fifty yards away, the crew of six, still clutching their half-empty mess-tins, bolted like rabbits and disappeared into a slit trench by the side of the pit. The sergeant spat out the mouthful of food he was about to swallow, as being the quickest way to get rid of it.

" Cover . . ." he echoed at the top of *his* voice, but it was drowned immediately by the sudden barking of all the Bofors in the area.

Crouched in their narrow ditch, tingling with expectation of their first dive-bombing ordeal, the six men all peered upwards, curiosity stronger than any other emotion, tense and breathing heavily.

Above the blue sky was alive with the white tufts of the bursting Bofors shells. Thousands of feet beyond the dotted screen the watchers in the trench saw the leading 'plane do a half-roll and dive (so it seemed) straight for them. Down it came at a terrific speed, at the same time piercing the air with a maniacal high-pitched scream that froze their blood, and for the moment bound them petrified, staring upwards. Then, as if on a common impulse, the six men hurled themselves down, down, as flat as they possibly could wedge themselves into the bottom of the trench, seized with a double fear that for the instant deprived them of all rational thought. Nothing mattered except to hide themselves from this winged thunderbolt that was hurling itself straight at their very hearts from the summits of the sky. Nothing mattered but to hide from this fearful nerve-shattering scream, this demon laugh, that grew louder and louder as it came nearer and nearer, searching them out, each of them individually, louder and louder, high above the bark of the Bofors, unearthly, diabolical.

" Gawd ! . . . What's happening to us ? " said the gun-layer with unsteady lips. He found it difficult to speak, and the words sounded like an inward prayer forced to the surface under torture.

No one else spoke. Words were beyond their power. The only sounds they could have uttered were inarticulate sounds of their gripping fears, and these they were choking back, still ashamed to show the terror that had momentarily overtaken them. They were suffering under that illusion that afflicts all men, however brave, when subjected to their first dive-bombing attack—the terrible, ineradicable belief that you yourself have been singled out specially for destruction, that the diving 'plane has seen you personally, and is coming straight for you, and that nothing on God's earth can stop it. On top of this, the fearful long-drawn shriek, as if of triumph over YOU, the destined and inescapable victim. A man must have more than nerves of iron to remain unaffected by such an experience. He must be utterly devoid of the slightest spark of imagination. In fact, not a man at all. Something of a lower species.

Only brief seconds had elapsed since the six men first cowered in the trench—no longer than the time taken for the leading Stuka to half complete its head-long three-hundred miles an hour dive from a height of ten thousand feet. But with that harrowing scream filling their ears, unnerving them, and gripped with the agony of that wait for the thunderbolt to strike them, Time, for every man in the trench lost all values. It might have been years.

Not far away the Troop Commander and the G.P.O crouched in an angle of the wall of the farmhouse. They also, to begin with, had been impelled by an overpowering curiosity to watch proceedings. Spellbound, they saw the leading Stuka dive, straight for *them*, so they thought. If they could have spoken each would have uttered the same words : " He's

75

coming to bomb ME." They, too, found themselves
petrified by the unhuman scream. They saw the dive
continue. The 'plane was now only four hundred
feet from the ground. Nothing surely could stop it
from crashing—into THEM. Suddenly they saw
three bombs released. As they dropped the machine
instantaneously stopped falling, and shot up into the
sky again at an incredibly steep angle. And at the
same moment they became aware of the crescendo
scream of the second 'plane making, in turn, its dive.

The first group of bombs landed amid the Bofors
emplacements. One of the second salvo made a direct
hit in the Bofors gun-pit that was nearest to B-Troop
position. A second before the G.P.O. had been staring
very fixedly at that Bofors, repeating to himself :

" Damn good . . . damn good. . . ."

Like the six men in the trench, the G.P.O. had been
considerably shaken up. He was now making a
powerful effort to recover himself by concentrating
his attention on the Bofors gun crew, which in the
midst of this terrifying, screaming hell, continued
coolly firing. The sight braced him up like a tonic.
It was something to take his mind off these infernal,
nerve-shattering screams.

" Damn good . . . damn good. . . ."

He was quite unconscious of paying tribute to the
gallant Bofors gunners. He just continued to repeat
the words automatically, even desperately, for his own
salvation.

Then, as the bomb burst in the pit, he saw the
wreck of the brave little gun hurled bodily into the
air. The gunners staggered blindly for a moment or
two in all directions, dropped to the ground, and
moved no more.

The remaining salvos of the first attack fell about
thirty yards from B-Troop position, close enough for

the Troop Commander and the G.P.O. to be shaken
by the blast. It also shook them out of their temporary stupor, and they raced for the protection of
the cellar. Before proceeding more than ten yards
the second dive caught them. Bombs burst behind
and in front of them. They flung themselves face
downwards, clawing at the earth, trying to embed
themselves into it. And every now and then the
ground, shaken by the explosions, seemed to rise and
smite them in the face.

Within the slit trench the six men also instinctively
endeavoured to press themselves deeper into the earth.
None dared raise a head to see what was happening
outside. They crouched together, quivering, each
fighting in his own way against the panic swelling in
his heart. There was every excuse for them. The
start of the attack had been nerve-shattering enough.
But now the nine Stukas had got into their stride.
They were diving automatically, one on top of the
other, cutting the air into ribbons with their fiendish
screech. Long before one had finished another began,
then another. The whole universe seemed to be
shredded into a tangle of terror-raising screams,
against which the actual detonation of the falling
bombs appeared a negligible trifle.

The occupants of the trench could not be expected
to know in this, the first few seconds of their first
experience, that those menacing screams, in themselves, had as much power to harm them as the shrill
whistles of the expresses flying through Clapham
Junction on a wet, misty morning. They could not
be expected to know that the terror of dive-bombing
is largely the terror of the Unknown, and that it
cannot be successfully instilled into the same individual twice. As for the other illusion, that the Stuka
has singled out YOU personally for attack, that you

are like a highly-charged electro-magnet drawing the 'plane irresistibly towards you in defiance of your will—that, too, resembles a conjuror's trick, astounding the first time, but quickly seen through. The truth is that, apart from the initial panic it may create, a dive-bombing attack is far less devastating than well-directed artillery fire. The dive-bomber aims, misses, and is just as likely to miss again and again, for he has no means of correcting his mistake. The big gun, five miles away from you, completely hidden from sight, drops one shell behind you and another in front, and the third very likely on top of you. The gun's " misses " *are* corrected. You really *are* being watched all the time. No. Of the two it is not the pilot in the Stuka just overhead who can " find " you. It is the unseen artillery observer.

Had the six men in the trench been told this they would not have believed it. They would not even have heard it. Their minds were too shattered for coherent thought. Five minutes had passed and the attack was at its height. The incessant, piercing, menacing screams appalled them. Their ignorance of what was happening outside drove them to imagine unbelievable terrors. They still fought, each in his own way, against utter surrender to panic, but each second the trench grew more highly charged with its dangerous atmosphere. The tinder was there. All it awaited was the spark. And anything at any moment might create that spark. The burly gunlayer, who had not spoken a word since his first ejaculation, crouched with head almost between his knees, fists pressed hard as as he could press them against his ears. His great shoulders, hunched as if to ward off a blow, trembled like a jelly. Two gunners huddled next to him, stared at one another with terror-stricken eyes, their complexion ghastly grey. An unspoken

query distorted their faces.   Words were beyond them.
Only their lips shook.   Otherwise they were frozen
stiff with horror.

The No. 3 on the gun, who was not much more than
a boy, continually plucked nervously at the sergeant's
sleeve to attract his attention.

" What is it, sergeant ? . . . What is it, sergeant ?
. . . What is it, sergeant ? . . ." he kept on beseech-
ingly, in a pitiful, infantile babble, that never ceased
for an instant.

Down the sergeant's lean face the sweat poured
in streams.   It manifested the tremendous effort he
was making to hold himself together.   He could see
the No. 3's lips moving, but remained quite oblivious
of what the speaker said.   He kept on nodding
mechanically, as if in cordial agreement with him.
Chiefly, however, the sergeant fixed his eyes on the
remaining gunner, a thin spare man of nearly forty,
whose limbs twitched violently, and whose wild
glances rove incessantly up and down the trench
like those of a trapped animal.   The sergeant knew
what was in the gunner's mind.   He was fighting
against the same impulse himself—the powerful urge
to escape from this narrow slit of a prison, to rush
out into the open, to move, to feel the relief of movement.   He might have done it had he not retained
just sufficient mind to realise that if he did leave the
trench he would simply dart backwards and forwards,
helplessly, stupidly, like a chicken with its head cut off.

Outside, two Stukas dived almost simultaneously,
with screams splitting the air with a terrifying dis-
cord.   They sounded as if they were diving straight
into the trench.   For the twitching gunner it proved
the last straw.   Uttering an incoherent cry, he shot
to his feet, and trampling over his crouching comrades, began to clamber out of the end of the trench.

This action had the effect of breaking the spell under which the sergeant had been labouring. Here was something normal that he could understand. A breach of discipline that he must stamp on. He flung his arms round the gunner's waist, and struggled to drag him back into the trench.

" No, you don't," he shouted.

" Let me go . . . Let me go, you bastard . . ." screamed the gunner, endeavouring to kick him off.

" Now don't you be silly. Where would you go if I did leave hold of you ? " the sergeant said soothingly, tightening his grip.

The gunner managed to raise his head just above the top of the trench. Desperately he gazed round him at the level earth. Anything to get out of the sergeant's grip. Any excuse to run, run.

Then his eye seized upon something—something he could turn cunningly to his own purpose. Something to compel the sergeant to let him go.

" The Captain and Mr. Vernon are down," he screamed. " I'm going over to bring 'em in."

The sergeant's reply was to hurl the man back into the trench. He thrust his own head over the top. Thirty yards away the bodies of the Troop Commander and the G.P.O. lay stretched on the ground, face downwards, without a movement.

Like the gunner, the sergeant thought they were dead. He withdrew his head.

" Because the Captain and Mr. Vernon have got theirs, that's no reason why you should get yours. Understand," he said curtly to the gunner, who was now whimpering at the bottom of the trench.

At that moment a salvo of three bombs burst with a deafening roar only a few yards from the trench. The earth shook. The blast flung the six men in a heap. A shower of debris rained on them.

When they recovered from the shock, it was to enter into a new and strange world—a world un-peopled by hideous screams. A world of deathly silence, itself uncanny.

The attack was over. It had lasted in all about ten minutes. Those three bombs were the farewell. From far away came the faint drone of the departing Stukas.

Within the trench the six men stared at each other, still breathing painfully, still trembling. The ser-geant was the first to make a move. He thrust his head over the top of the trench, and was astonished to see the Troop Commander and the G.P.O. walking, rather unsteadily, to the Troop Command Post cellar. For the first time he noticed how violently he was sweating, and mopped his streaming face with the back of his hand. He leaned heavily against the side of the trench ; like the others, crumpled and limp and weary after the ordeal.

" Take Post . . . Fresh Target . . ."

The G.P.O.'s voice rang out. New fire orders had arrived from the Battery Command Post. Mercifully the men in the trench were suddenly summoned back into the world they understood without being given time to dwell on the horrors of the unknown.

" Take Post . . ." roared the sergeant, leaping from the trench. " Come on, all of you. Tumble out of that cot."

A minute later the sound of their own guns was like sweet music to their ears. They barely noticed the little procession of stretcher-bearers, trotting with their three stretchers from the rear towards the shattered Bofors gun-pit.

*   *   *   *   *

Later in the day the G.P.O. found himself at the Battery Command Post giving the Major an account of the attack.

81   F

"A nasty business," said the Major, when he had finished. "Thank Heaven the Troop didn't suffer at all. I suppose the Bofors gave us away."

Everybody was surprised that the G.P.O. did not jump to agree. But he remained silent. Three little pictures haunted him. One, the gallant Bofors gunners working their gun with drill-like precision in a moment when the world seemed to be coming to an end. Two, the wreck of the gun hurled into the air amid its dead and dying crew. Three, six stretcher-bearers walking heavily away from the gun-pit with their motionless loads.

In face of such pictures there could be no criticism, no recrimination.

A JOB OF WORK

V—A Job of Work

LATER, I shall come to the incident itself in which Lieutenant Reginald Ellington of the 666th Field Regiment R.A. figured as hero.

Hero is the word understood of, and approved by the general public. But it is not the term under which Reggie Ellington's comrades ever consider him. And, of course, it is the very last word he would dream of in connection with himself.

Upon this subject of gallant deeds and decorations there is a noteworthy difference of thought between the population of the Army itself and what may be called their civilian relatives—in other words, the outside public. It may be accepted as a truth beyond contradiction that the Army knows all there is to be known about decorations, their worth, their significance, and sometimes their insignificance. They have standards and appreciations that are not always identical with those held outside its ranks. The generous-minded, sentimental public love to have their heroes. They take them to their heart and glamourise them. But to the people within the Army there is no glamour about a medal. Even a V.C.—which takes a bit of winning—does not carry hero-worship with it. This, of course, must not be taken to mean that the Army does not care for decorations just as much as everybody else. The Army does. But it is very reluctant to regard them as a badge of superhuman courage or ability, by which one man is to be for ever distinguished beyond his fellows. They like decorations in the Army, but they like them mainly as an indication that a job of work has been well done. The only possible exception to this is to be found in the case of the V.C. to win which a man must face almost certain death. It is recognised that here is something a bit more out of the way than a " job of work." It is also recognised that a man will do things in the heat of battle that in cold blood would make him sick merely to think about. So the soft-pedal comes down on the hero-worship, even with the V.C.

The Army nurtures no illusions about " gongs," their own expressive slang for medals. They know that the man disporting one is as likely to be no braver than the man without. They know that many factors have to fall just right for the winning of one. And they know that a principal factor is luck. All may be brave, but not all may be lucky enough to have their deeds noticed. A man may miss a V.C. merely because his gallant behaviour happens not to be seen by " someone in authority " —an essential condition. Opportunity is another potent factor. One man may go through a long campaign and never a chance of qualifying for a " gong " comes within a mile of him. Another has opportunities thrust upon him in his very first engagement. He simply cannot miss them. There still remains the mystery of the final adjudication—how one bit of work comes to be acknowledged by the powers that be as worth an M.C. or an M.M. while another, to all intents and purposes just as meritorious, goes unrewarded. Illustrative of this is the story of a gunner subaltern in the last war, who was recommended on four different occasions for the M.C. but never received more than a " mention in despatches." He was recommended a fifth time, and got it. Ultimate recognition came to him because in the middle of an action he had thrown a bucket of water over the hessian camouflage net covering a gun-pit, after it had been set on fire by the flash from one of the guns. The deed involved him in no particular danger. He happened to be standing near a bucket at the time, and acted with presence of mind. That was all. As a " gong-earner " the exploit could not be compared with any of the previous four that had not been considered worthy of the M.C. The subaltern knew it, and was always very shy of his belated ribbon. It is the complete understanding of these fortuitous factors governing decorations that gives the Army its very clear perspective on the subject.

The Army divides all D.S.O.'s, M.C.'s, M.M.'s, and D.C.M.'s into two distinct classes. The first are known as " Immediate Awards," and they are given for gallantry or distinguished conduct in action. Your recommendation for one of these goes in from the Regiment to the Division directly the action is over. Sometimes this will be the same day. The C.O. may make it his last job that night. There is as little delay as possible. Hence the term : " Immediate Awards."

The second group are familiarly known in the Army as " Ration Honours," and though the " high-ups " may be slightly shocked by the irreverence of the phrase, nevertheless it very neatly sums up their character. They come along automatically, like rations, after an action in which a Division or more has been engaged. It may be one, two, or three months after. But they arrive. So many D.S.O.'s,

so many M.C.'s, so many M.M.'s and D.C.M.'s for
each Division. These in turn are cut up and allotted
to each regiment that took part in the action. If,
as often happens, there are no outstanding cases of
gallantry still deserving recognition, the C.O. of the
regiment or battalion holds a conference with the
Majors to decide who shall receive them for general
good work. Much like the distribution of good conduct medals at school.

Therefore, it will easily be understood that a D.S.O.,
M.C., M.M. or D.C.M. may mean many different
things. If it be an " Immediate Award " it implies
a good deal more than if it be a " Ration Honour."
Generally speaking, " Immediate Awards " are individually earned honours. A Colonel or Major may
get a D.S.O. simply because his battalion or regiment,
or company or battery, has been doing well. They
cannot get less, because the M.C. is not awarded to
anyone over the rank of captain. On the other hand,
a D.S.O. can be won by a subaltern and, speaking
generally again, if a subaltern gets the D.S.O. you
can bet your boots that it is worth far more than
the majority of D.S.O.'s handed out to Colonels and
Majors. A subaltern's D.S.O. is never a " Ration
Honour." It's more likely to be a near-miss to a
V.C.

Perhaps it is because the Army knows so much of
the " inside story " of decorations that the subject
is never a popular one for conversation among officers
or men. If the topic does crop up it is mentioned in
a very diffident manner, and the talk soon dies a
natural death. The last man in the world to tell
you how he won a " gong " is the wearer of the ribbon
himself. (I am speaking, of course, as in the Army.
Among his civilian friends he may feel less embarrassed.) Most of them wear their new ribbons

almost apologetically. "You'd have done the same if you'd been in my position," sums up the whole medal attitude. They can also be very touchy on the subject amongst their comrades. I recall a young gunner subaltern who, after being evacuated from Dunkirk, went home on leave, and the morning after saw to his horror that the newspapers had made a headline story of his winning the M.C. He felt so embarrassed that when he rejoined the regiment six days later he still hadn't put up the ribbon.

"Why aren't you wearing it ? " asked the Colonel.

"I'm very annoyed about the whole affair, sir" he replied. "I hope none of you think I had anything to do with that newspaper stuff."

"My dear fellow, we never dreamed for a moment that you had," said the Colonel. "Let me see you with that ribbon on to-morrow. That's an order."

Having seen a good many "gongs" cleaned up by the B.E.F. in Flanders and France I am able, without hesitation, to add my testimony to the bulk of evidence supporting the theory that there exists no specific "brave man" type. A lot of preconceived ideas about who would do well and who wouldn't went by the board as soon as men came under fire. Some of the frail-looking rabbits did magnificently. Some of the great hefty fellows, real bruisers, turned out hopeless. And it was the same with temperament as with physique. Which only goes to show that human nature is as incalculable on the battlefield as it is elsewhere.

And this brings me back to Lieutenant Reggie Ellington, whose externals were not of the type usually associated with candidates for battlefield honours. Reggie had the pallor of a lily. He was frail, and somewhat drooping. If he represented any type at all, it was the youthful man-about-town, dandified,

and a bit affected. Later on, we were to remember
that if Reggie exhibited the paleness of the lily, he
also possessed its coolness. We remembered occasions
when he had talked to brass-hats as if he were doing
them a favour. (Surprisingly enough, they'd take it
from him.) Winning an M.C. *would* come as child's
play to a youth who could do this, we realised. But
this was only wisdom after the event. So was our
realisation that his treatment of serious matters as a
joke, and his apparent lack of any sense of responsibility, had all the time been merely a pose. Before
the war, Reggie had " been something " in his father's
business in the City. He affected to find army life
unendurable without his portable wireless set, and his
cigar in the evening. Wherever he was, and whatever the critical conditions during the Retreat, he
never missed his cigar. Whatever else had to be
jettisoned, he clung to his cigar box and wireless set
to the grim end. And it was grim enough, in all
conscience. Dunkirk beach, strewn with its dead and
dying, a pall of smoke blotting out the sky, the promenade one sheet of flame, the German shells bursting
among the dunes, the dive-bombers distributing their
final dose of death and destruction before nightfall.
And in the middle of the horrors, Reggie Ellington
seated calmly on the sand in front of his crooning
wireless, smoking his very last cigar. Just one man
of many who, in the hectic days of the preceding
three weeks, had done a good job of work.

*   *   *   *   *

On a warm, sunny, handsome morning late in May
K-Battery of the 666th Field Regiment R.A. found
itself in action supporting a local advance by the
British infantry to the south-west of Maroeuil. Their

twelve 25-pounders occupied positions behind Vimy
Ridge, and an O.P. had been established on top of
the Ridge to the west of Givenchy, from which their
fire was being directed. As the morning progressed
the British attack was pushed forward with considerable rapidity till eventually the battle passed
beyond reasonable control from the O.P. The Observation Officer could see shells exploding in the distance,
some miles away, and tracer shells from the anti-tank
guns bowling through the air like red-hot cricket balls.
But the conflict had moved so far off that even with
his powerful binoculars he was unable to distinguish with
certainty between the German positions and our own.

" Get me the Major on the 'phone," he said to
the telephonist.

In a few seconds the Battery Command Post replied.

" The advance has gone so far, sir," the O.P. officer
reported, " that it is impossible to fire accurately and
give the infantry close support. Shall I move forward ? "

" No. Stay where you are," answered the Major.
" I'll send out a Forward Observation Officer."

At that moment Lieutenant Reginald Ellington
happened to stroll into the Command Post, looking
very dapper and, unlike everybody else, not be-
draggled in battle-dress, but garnitured in smart
breeches, top-boots and tunic.

" Here's a job for you, Reggie," said the Major.
" The O.P. on the Ridge reports that the battle is
out of our control. It's necessary to send out an
F.O.O. Get off at once and establish contact with
the 2nd Battalion of the North Ridings."

" And where are they likely to be lurking ? "
drawled Reggie.

The Major pointed out on the map the forward
area of the advance.

" Somewhere around there," he said. " When you
find Battalion H.Q. wireless back where the forward
troops have got to, and then engage any targets their
Colonel desires us to take on. You may have to
hunt about a bit, from the pace at which they are
moving. It'll be safer if you take Toc."

Toc was the armoured vehicle, somewhat similar to
a Bren-gun carrier, usually utilised by Forward
Observation Officers when engaged in liaison work with
front line infantry.

" No, thank you, Major," drawled Reggie with slow
emphasis. " I won't look at Toc. I've no confidence
in her. I prefer my own truck. It may not stop
bullets, but I know it will keep going."

So, in his glistening top-boots, Reggie Ellington
started forth in search of B.H.Q. of the 2nd North
Ridings, sitting beside his driver with a wireless
operator in the rear of the canvas-hooded truck.

Now, it is no easy business tracking down B.H.Q.
of an attacking force in these days of moving warfare.
Often it is never in the same spot for half an hour
together. As the situation changes so does B.H.Q.
Backwards and forwards, to right and to left, sometimes over several miles of country. You chase it in
short spurts, continually stopping to ask questions,
preferably of men of the particular unit. But if they
can give you an answer it is rarely more than a
direction to the last place B.H.Q. was seen at. And
by the time you arrive there the chances are they have
flown, and you have to begin all over again. Hours
can be spent in this pastime. But the fun of it soon
palls, especially on hot, dry, dusty, pavé roads.

Reggie's truck took the road over the Ridge, then
down the winding road through Neuville St. Vaast
towards Mont St. Eloi. Here he came into contact
with the first indications of the battle—German

prisoners in little groups being rounded up in a field,
wounded and dying soldiers by the roadside, ambu-
lances returning from the direction of the fighting,
despatch riders tearing backwards and forwards. His
own troubles now commenced. He inquired of a
wounded sergeant the whereabouts of B.H.Q.

" You're asking me, sir," was the encouraging reply.
" There isn't what you call a definite B.H.Q. The
Colonel's following up the battle in his truck. That's
all the B.H.Q. I know of. And when you find it you
may find that he's walked off over the fields to direct
the attack."

With this information Reggie had to be content.
It was correct enough, as he found to his sorrow
during the next hour and a half, which he spent
zig-zagging about in the blazing sun panting for a
glimpse of the Colonel's truck. He asked scores of
questions and received scores of conflicting replies.
He chased his quarry along roads, up lanes, and across
paths—anywhere where his own truck would carry him.
After a long while the only net result appeared to be
that he was closely approaching the battle line. He
could smell the slight whiff of cordite in the air.
Machine-gun and rifle fire rattled round him. The
sharp crack of the anti-tank guns sounded almost at
his elbow.

" Hand me those spare earphones," he said to the
wireless operator.

The operator passed them through the hole in the
canvas hood at the rear of the truck. Reggie affixed
them under his tin hat, picked up the microphone
and got into direct touch with the Major.

" I'm still looking for B.H.Q.," he said. " This
Colonel's name doesn't appear by any chance to be
Pimpernel, does it ? Christian name, Scarlet ? I'm
still cruising about in hope."

93

And while the truck proceeded on its man hunt, Reggie continued to regale the Major with a running commentary on the progress of the battle, in a voice as calm as a B.B.C. announcer narrating the fat stock prices. The Major could hear the noise of the battle over the microphone. He knew it was a pretty hot spot. They could see enough from the old O.P. on the Ridge to gather that.

" I wish you'd taken Toc," he said.

" We're doing quite well, thank you, Major," laughed Reggie. " All that's missing is the Colonel."

At last, just after noon, Reggie found him. After so many disappointments he could hardly believe it when he saw the truck standing by the side of a narrow road. The Colonel wasn't within. As the wounded sergeant had predicted, he had footed it across some fields to maintain better observation on the progress of the attack. Thither Reggie followed him.

The Colonel and the Adjutant of the 2nd North Ridings were sitting under semi-cover in a little hollow behind a screen of thin bushes.

" I'm F.O.O. from K-Battery, sir," said Reggie, introducing himself. " Have you any jobs we can do for you ? "

" Glad to see you, my boy," replied the Colonel. " Yes, you can be useful in one or two directions. See that wood yonder ? We're getting opposition from machine-gun and trench-mortar fire there."

He pointed to a cluster of houses a mile away.

" That's another useful target," he said. " They've mounted two anti-tank guns there, and are giving my Bren-gun carriers no end of trouble."

The Colonel studied his map for half a minute.

" After that, concentrate on these spots," he said, indicating them with his finger. " They're likely forming-up points for an enemy counter attack."

94

A second thought occurred to him. " I might want you to put a smoke screen over that wood, if your H.E. fire isn't effective," he said. " Can you do it ? How long would it take ? "

Reggie produced a handkerchief and held it at arm's length to test the speed and direction of the wind.

" Not an ideal day for smoke, sir," he announced. " I can't guarantee a screen. We can try if you really want it."

Before returning to his truck to commence operations Reggie stood up in the little hollow for a while, studying the prospective targets through his binoculars. The Colonel and the Adjutant remained seated. Having noted all the features that were necessary, Reggie lowered his glasses and turned towards the Colonel for a last word. The Colonel was merely a heap on the ground. Dead. Shot through the head.

Speechless, Reggie jerked his head round to the Adjutant. He was another crumpled heap. Dead. Shot through the head, likewise.

The suddenness of it staggered him. A few moments before he had been one of three live, hearty men. Now he was standing alone, with a corpse to his right and another to his left. No lily could have been paler than Reggie's face at that moment. Involuntarily, he cringed as if shrinking from the third bullet of an incomplete trio. He almost imagined it was lurking somewhere in the air near by. Then he dived for cover.

" Good God ! . . . What's happened ? . . ." exclaimed a voice behind him.

It was the Second-in-Command of the 2nd North Ridings, dusty and perspiring, who had just arrived to report strong enemy opposition on the left flank.

" I hardly know," replied Reggie in a shaken voice. " I was taking a peep at some targets through my glasses, and when I looked round . . ."

"Those bloody machine-guns . . ." the Second-in-Command exploded, with a jerk of his head towards the wood to which Reggie's attention had already been drawn by the Colonel.

He knelt down and satisfied himself that both men were dead.

"All right. . . . I'll see to this. . . . A dreadful business. . . ." he said.

"The Colonel gave me some targets he wanted taken on," Reggie observed. "P'raps you'd like to look them over."

"They're O.K. for the present," said the Second-in-Command, after a swift inspection. "You needn't bother about those houses now. We've accounted for them."

And, still very pale and shaken, Reggie hurried back across the fields to his truck.

Now, up to the present Reggie had done nothing at all to bring him within a mile of a "recommendation." He had just fulfilled the ordinary obligations of his duty, and it was merely by accident that he had become a participator of the grim little drama in the B.H.Q. in the hollow. His "good job of work" was to date from the moment he returned to his truck. Remember, it was that and nothing else. There was nothing spectacular about it at all. No glitter or glamour. No gallery stuff. It was just a good job of work. Exactly the sort of thing that the men in the Army like to see, and know how to appreciate. A piece of work typical of that which wins the bulk of the M.C.'s and M.M.'s whose ribbons you see displayed on the breasts of the B.E.F. in 1940. And that is the reason why it is being recorded here.

Reggie's first necessity was to equip himself with an O.P. He scouted around a bit, and came to the conclusion that though there were several possibilities, there was nothing good enough for him. This was a matter of conscience. Had he possessed less he would have accepted what was going, and saved himself further trouble. No one would have blamed him. No one would ever have known anything about it. He could have installed himself in some fairly peaceful spot where he had a fair view of the sector, and just carried on. Quite a lot of people would have done so. And thought none the worse of themselves. Not so Reggie. Unable to satisfy his requirements behind the battle line, he decided to convey himself and his truck as far forward as he could get.

Driving along the road in the direction of the attacking infantry, he encountered the Second-in-Command (now the O.C.) of the 2nd North Ridings, who inquired where he had established his O.P.

" Here," replied Reggie, " in the truck. I think I can do better if I get a bit closer to your line."

" Fine idea . . . if you can dodge the dirt. It's coming over pretty thick."

There was no need to tell Reggie this. A couple of shells had burst in a field to his left only a minute before, and the air sang with bullets. He got into touch with the Battery Command Post and informed the Major of his intentions. The Major was not enthusiastic. He foresaw the truck knocked out, all the trouble of sending out a new F.O.O., and a lot of valuable time wasted thereby.

" Be damn careful what you're up to," he said. " There's no point in doing anything foolhardy."

" Wouldn't dream of it, Major," Reggie replied. " This is strictly business."

He proceeded along the road, turned off at a junction on the left, passed through the infantry reserve line lying behind a hedge, and a little farther along parked his truck in dead ground under a slope. Then, alone, he crawled up to the crest to see what he could see. He found himself gazing down on the infantry only a hundred yards in front, with a first-class view of the battle.   Every now and then little groups of men rose from the earth, darted forward a few yards, and sank down into fresh cover.   The edge of the thick wood half a mile in front flickered continually with the red stabs of flame from the German rifle and machine-gun fire.   Farther back, bigger flashes denoted the presence of trench mortars.   In addition there was an occasional pale, orangey-green flash, which Reggie knew to be the mark of a German infantry gun.   The trench-mortar bombs came swishing through the air, shooting up fountains of earth as they exploded fifty yards in front of him.   Here and there, a bit of hedge or a tree that had been set on fire, blazed furiously.   Reggie noted all this.   But the principal thing he noted was his own perfect view of the wood.

He crawled off the crest and hurried back to his truck.

" Give me the remote control set," he said to the wireless operator.

The remote control set consists of a small drum of wire and a box-like contraption, into one end of which you can plug a microphone and earphones.   It comes in handy when you do not wish to bring your truck stationary right in front of the enemy.

The wireless operator attached the loose end of the drum wire to the set in the rear of the truck, and with the box and the leather pouch containing the microphone and earphones slung over his shoulder, Reggie remounted the slope, unwinding the wire from the drum as he proceeded.   He flattened himself out below the crest, connected the box to the metal drum, plugged in the earphones and microphone, and was ready to commence operations.   He was now in direct communication with the Battery. Back in the truck the wireless operator sat, silent with the earphones on, listening to the conversation. His one job now was to turn the switch from transmission to receiver whenever he heard either speaker say : " Over."

" 2-Troop Target. . . . Don Control. . . . Charge 2. . . . Zero, 356 degrees. . . . Angle of sight, 20 minutes elevation. . . . Left ranging. . . . 6,200. . . . Fire. Over . . .," ordered Reggie.

The telephonist of Don-Troop repeated it back.

" Correct," said Reggie. " Over .   ."

Almost immediately came the report : " Shot 3 . . Over," and the shot whistled over his head.

Reggie lifted his glasses and saw it burst two hundred yards minus the left-hand corner of the wood.

" More 2 degrees . . . 6,600. . . . Over . . ." he ordered.

" Shot 3 . . . Over," came the voice of the G.P.O.

This time Reggie was gratified to see the shell " plomp " into the wood, in the centre, fairly deep in. He dropped a hundred yards in range, ordered one-round gunfire, and half a minute later eight rounds burst in a line along the front edge of the wood. He decided to add fifty yards to bring it right on the edge of the wood, and, this proving satisfactory, ordered ten rounds gunfire, interval one minute.

The red stabs of flame in the wood dwindled and ceased. Reggie, with no little personal satisfaction saw the North Ridings commence advancing in short rushes. This was the sort of artillery support the infantry could appreciate to the utmost. They pushed on confidently. When they were about fifty yards from the edge of the wood, Reggie stopped the Battery fire. He saw the riflemen go forward into the wood at a run, covered on the flanks by the Bren-gunners. That job was done.

So he continued during the afternoon, moving up
with the front-line infantry when it advanced, halting
when the advance was held up, taking on his targets
as they cropped up.   The infantry wondered what was
happening.   The little groups he passed up and down
the roads regarded the pallid officer in the artillery
truck with a faint amusement.   Their private opinion
was that he was " a bit of a mug."   They took the
sternly realistic view that anyone messing about in
front who wasn't absolutely compelled to be there,
was asking for trouble.   And deserved it !   They
rather overlooked the important fact that, being where
he was, Reggie could judge to within fifty yards when
to stop his fire and when to increase his range.   Also,
that that fact had an important bearing on their own
individual lives.

On the left flank, with Reggie in his truck only a
hundred yards behind the foremost troops, there
occurred a hold-up.   The Second-in-Command hurried
up to him.

" A couple of tanks are coming up that road on the
left, a mile away," he said.   " Do what you can
for us."

Noting where the road came into view, Reggie sent
down to the guns a G.F. Target, a warning to the
Battery that it was a moving target so they'd have to
look slippy.   He quickly ranged on the bit of road
and ordered : " Fire by order . . . two rounds gunfire. . . ."

Miles away, behind Vimy Ridge, the guns were
loaded and ready to fire.

With the earphones clamped to his head, Reggie
kept his glasses fastened on the distant curve of the
road, waiting.

" There they come," shouted the Second-in-Command, excitedly.   But before the words had passed

his lips, Reggie had shouted " Fire .   ." into the microphone.

The first salvo of shells landed in the road just in front of the two tanks. They stopped and appeared to hesitate. As the second salvo dropped in nearly the same spot they turned and disappeared in the direction they had come. Reggie increased the range for his third salvo. It fell, of course, out of his view.

" A parting kick in the pants," he explained, as he removed the earphones.

" A neat little job," returned the Second-in-Command with enthusiasm. " Thanks. Now we can push on."

Once more the artillery truck became a part of the infantry advance. It seemed to bear a charmed life. For the bulk of the afternoon it had dodged about on roads plastered by shell fire and swept by machine-gun bullets. One shell fragment had torn a rent in the canvas cover and dented the driver's tin hat. In addition, the hood sported five bullet holes. Reggie possessed another in the sleeve of his beautiful tunic, and the earth showered over him by a trench-mortar bomb had effectually removed the gloss from his shining top-boots. Pale, and perceptibly drawn, he still remained nonchalant. He continually told the driver how lucky they were not to have taken Toc, the armoured O.P., but to be able to nip about quickly without fear of breakdown in their light truck. The driver was very non-committal. . . .

Late in the afternoon Reggie discovered he had lost touch for the time being with the forward troops. Altogether they had advanced about four miles. Latterly the advance had been over fields where it was impossible for Reggie's truck to follow. For a quarter of an hour or more he had been searching for a road leading, roughly, in the required direction. Finally he found one, as he thought, and sped forward.

The road conducted him over the top of a small hill into a village. Save for a few stray rifle shots in the distance everything seemed quiet as he approached. He came to the conclusion that the infantry had pressed right on. So he parked his car in the court-yard of a farm and climbed to a loft in order to get a good view. He was rather surprised when he arrived there to discover no signs of any actual fighting. But this surprise was as nothing to his next. Looking up the village street, he suddenly saw a couple of German motor-cyclists enter, followed by two lorry loads of German infantry.

His first thought was characteristic of Reggie : " I wonder what my first remark to them will be . . ."

His next was : " I must get out of here. . . . How the devil can I ? . . ."

At that moment inspiration descended upon Reggie. It came in the guise of a desperate measure. But nevertheless genuine inspiration it was.

He bolted from the loft and crept cautiously round the walls of the farmyard to his truck, expecting every moment to receive a bullet in his back. Nothing happened and, looking as if he'd seen a ghost, Reggie acquainted the driver and the wireless operator with the alarming facts.

" Keep very quiet," he said. " I'll tell you what I'm going to do. We haven't an earthly chance of making a dash for it down the road. So I'm going to get the battery to shell them. And while they're taking cover we'll clear out. See ? "

He read in their expressions their unspoken com-ments on his flash of inspiration.

" I know," he hastened to add, " we run a bit of risk from the shells ourselves, but it's that or—— Quick, give me the earphones."

In a few seconds he was through to the Battery and

had given them the village as a Battery target. Then the three of them sat in the truck and waited.

It was not a pleasant wait. It was a very long wait, as it seemed to them. Hours. Actually it was less than two minutes.

Then the first flock of shells screamed over their heads, crashing into roof-tops, on buildings, and into the road. Clouds of smoke and dust filled the air.

"Start the engine," Reggie yelled, with his mouth against the driver's ear, for the noise of the bursting shells was deafening.

The truck leaped forward through the entrance arch of the courtyard into the main street, with the driver's foot flat down on the accelerator. They fled past one of the German lorries, empty, which had been wrecked by a shell. The other they could not see. Nor did they see any Germans. As Reggie had hoped, they were too busy taking cover. Nevertheless, just before shaking the village off their wheels, a couple of rifles cracked and the canvas hood of the truck acquired another two mementos. That was all the damage.

A mile up the road the 2nd North Ridings, lying in the ditches awaiting the advance of the enemy, were astonished suddenly to see the artillery truck come tearing madly along from the direction of the village. Reggie halted a little further along when he encountered the Second-in-Command, and briefly explained what had happened.

"First time I've ever heard of a fellow making a Battery target of himself," the Second-in-Command grinned. "Very original. . . . D'you know, you've done us a grand turn. That village is our final objective for the day. Now we can push straight on and clean it up."

"All right," Reggie said calmly. "I'll lift the fire as you go in."

Shortly afterwards the 2nd North Ridings entered the village under the screen of what may be termed Reggie's own personal barrage. Reggie entered it, too. And its associations remained so unpleasant that he extracted a certain degree of comfort from sticking close all the time to the Second-in-Command.

He telephoned to the Battery Command Post, informing them that the day's work was over.

" I'll send along another F.O.O. to relieve you," replied the Major.

An hour later Reggie was back at the B.C.P. giving the Major a very abbreviated and formal account of his doings. He confined himself strictly to essentials. Among the many things he did not mention were the shooting of the North Ridings' Colonel and Adjutant in the little hollow, and the true origin of his last battery target. They were things he did not feel disposed to dwell upon. Besides looking paler than ever, he also felt a trifle sick. He craved to be alone for a bit. Not to have to talk to anybody.

As soon as he made his report he quitted the Command Post, collected his portable wireless set and his box of cigars from his kit, and conveyed them to an outhouse in the distant corner of the farmyard. There, sitting with his back against a truss of straw, he lit a cigar and tuned-in till he got music. Any music. It didn't matter what. He felt an overpowering need for re-adjustment. Re-adjustment of himself. To feel himself once more the Reggie Ellington that he knew so well and appreciated so much.

After a while, listening to the soft music, and puffing at his cigar, the magic began to work.

" Yes," he reflected. " A wireless set is a damned sensible thing. So is a cigar. But careering over the country doing what I've been doing all the afternoon is just simply damned idiotic."

It wasn't till later in the evening, when the Second-in-Command of the 2nd North Ridings 'phoned through to him that the Major realised for the first time what a good job of work Reggie had performed.

" I hope that pale-faced officer of yours got back safely," said the Second-in-Command. " He's a treasure. Saved us the loss of any amount of lives to-day, I consider."

And he proceeded to enlighten the Major.

After the conversation the Major sat for a minute or two thinking. Then he commenced to write. He headed his paper :

> " To O.C. 666th Field Regt., R.A.
>   Subject :—Recommendation."

and continued : " Lieutenant R. Ellington, on May —th, whilst acting as Forward Observation Officer, conducted the shooting of the Battery with great gallantry, and in so doing enabled the infantry to attain all its objectives."

The Major then followed with much of what has already been related, affixed his signature, and slipped the report in an envelope. Before sealing it, he inserted a private note to the Colonel :

> *" For the enclosed work I recommend Ellington for the Military Cross.*

He summoned a Don R.

" Take this up to R.H.Q. at once," he said.

ONE OF THOSE MYSTERIES

THE map co-ordinates of a new batch of defensive
fire tasks had just arrived from Division. In the
vaulted brick-roof cellar below the small white-
shuttered château where the 777th Field Regiment,
R.A., had established its headquarters, the Adjutant
sat studying a board on which was fastened a large
scale map of the area, covered with celluloid. Already
this celluloid top had been scored over heavily with
chinagraph pencils of various colours, red, blue, green,
mauve, yellow. To the uninitiated it appeared just
a confused tangle of lines and curves. Yet here the
knowing eye could read at a glance the exact disposition of the British Forces in the neighbourhood.
Not only did the map indicate the Divisional zones
and the inter-Brigade and inter-Battalion boundaries,
but also the battle-line, the forward defended localities
and our own outpost line in front. Here, too, was
depicted in different colours all the details that more
closely concerned the Adjutant—his own regimental
zone divided up into the Battery zones, and these in
turn marked with the gun positions.

At present the Adjutant was engrossed in the business of elaborating the colour scheme. Every now
and then, as the Regimental Orderly Officer who was
looking over his shoulder read out the co-ordinates, he

pencilled carefully on the celluloid a little circle.
Inside he inscribed D.F.1, D.F.2, and so on, these
marks denoting the positions of the Batteries' new
fire tasks and their relative importance. As each
circle came into being the Orderly Officer checked up
its position carefully from his list ; and the Adjutant,
to make sure of there being no mistake, repeated the
co-ordinates aloud. It was no job to be in a hurry
over.

For two days the regiment had been in action outside Givenchy. A straight road led from the château
to the Battery positions about three-quarters of a
mile further on. Although the gun areas on either
side of the road sustained a certain amount of bombing, R.H.Q. in the château had so far escaped attention. Flocks of German bombers passed over them
continually, but always on other business—so far.

It was half-past four in the afternoon. A thin
haze of cigarette smoke filled the cellar, rendered
visible by the sunshine that filtered in through a small,
dirty, square window just above ground level. An
old-fashioned but roomy arm-chair in faded red plush
had been commandeered from one of the upstairs
rooms in the château and installed in the cellar. It
represented comparative comfort, and the occupants
took it in turns to snatch short spells of sleep in it
whenever the chance offered. Just now the Colonel
held tenure. Fast asleep, with his tin hat tilted forward
half-way down his nose by the back of the chair, he
snored so vigorously that the Adjutant and the Orderly
Officer cast distressful glances at each other. Three
telephonists, with earphones clamped on, squatted on
the straw-covered floor beside their instruments. One
line connected with Division Headquarters, R.A., a
mile or so away at Petit Vimy. The other two linked
up with the Battery Command Posts. At regular

intervals these emitted a buzz, upon which the operator announced monotonously : " Line O.K."

The Adjutant drew another little circle on the celluloid, marked it D.F.5 and relinquished the stump of pencil.

" That's the last, isn't it ? " he said to the Orderly Officer. " I suppose we had better give a final check-up on the lot. You read the co-ordinates over again."

Scarcely had they commenced when the bell on the line to Division sounded.

" Brigade Major on the 'phone, sir," the telephonist announced, removing his own earphones as he handed the 'phone to the Adjutant.

" Is that you, Vernon ? " inquired the Brigade Major. " I've got withdrawal orders for you."

It was the last thing the Adjutant expected. His eyebrows shot up in surprise.

" Why, we've only just had a set of new fire tasks sent down," he said.

" Well, you can scrap 'em."

" Nothing wrong, is there ? "

" If you stay much longer where you are you'll find out," replied the Brigade Major with a short laugh. " You know, you are on the extreme right of our line. And your next-door neighbours were the French."

" What do you mean . . . ' were ' ? "

" That's it. They've cleared out. Your flank is in the air, old fellow. At any moment the new neigh-bours may move in : . . Germans. They're beginning to outflank you."

" Well, I'm damned," was all the Adjutant could find to say.

" We've got the orders ready for you here. Will you send an officer along for them at once ? Sooner the better," advised the Brigade Major.

"I will," said the Adjutant, still scarcely able to credit his ears.

"What's up?" inquired the Orderly Officer when the conversation ended.

"Another pigeon," replied the Adjutant tersely. "Some bird this time."

The Orderly Officer understood the allusion. The story of the carrier pigeon with orders, being overtaken by another who says : "Hurry up and get there. I've got the countermand," had obtained much popularity among R.H.Q.s.

"We're to wash out the fire tasks and prepare to withdraw instead," added the Adjutant, giving him the gist of the conversation. "I'll send Peter Forbes over for the orders at once."

He rang up Brigade Headquarters and asked to speak to Captain Peter Forbes, who was acting as liaison officer between his regiment and the infantry. The captain was not there, but they expected him back at any moment.

"As soon as Captain Forbes does come will you tell him to go to Division Headquarters, R.A., and collect some orders that are awaiting him and bring them straight back to me? Thank you," said the Adjutant, replacing the 'phone.

"The bright side of all this," he continued to the Orderly Officer, "is that we are now provided with a good excuse for stopping the loud-speaker."

He took a couple of steps towards the arm-chair, and rapped three times with his knuckles on the crown of the Colonel's tin hat, cutting short the career of a magnificent and reverberating snore.

"I've been asleep," observed the Colonel as usual, sitting up very wide awake.

"Yes, sir. We know," said the Adjutant. "I

wouldn't have disturbed you, but orders for withdrawal are coming down at once from Division."

He explained the new situation as it had been outlined to him by the Brigade Major.

"Send a warning to the batteries to prepare to withdraw," said the Colonel. "Tell them orders will follow later. Meanwhile, begin packing up here."

Not until their preparations for departure were considerably advanced did the Adjutant begin to feel more than a trifle worried at the non-appearance of the withdrawal orders. Divisional Headquarters, R.A., being little more than a mile away, there seemed no justification for the delay. He waited another ten minutes, and then as the orders had still not come to hand, 'phoned through to Division H.Q.

"Has Captain Forbes been there to collect orders?" he asked.

"Oh, yes," was the reply. "He collected them some time ago."

The Adjutant replaced the 'phone.

"They say Peter left with the orders some time ago," he informed the Colonel. "What the devil can he be doing all this while?"

At that moment Captain Peter Forbes himself descended the steps of the cellar, and appeared rather surprised to notice signs that a remove was being contemplated.

"You've been a hell of a time, Peter," exclaimed the Adjutant. "Let's have those orders."

Peter stared, first at him and then at the Colonel, blankly.

"What orders?" he asked.

"Oh, quit fooling. This is urgent," said the Adjutant, becoming heated. "The orders you collected from Divisional H.Q. of course. What else do you think I mean?"

"I haven't any orders," said Peter very definitely.

It was the Adjutant's turn to look blank.

"Haven't you been to Div. H.Q. ? " he demanded.

"No."

"Nonsense. You must have been. Only just now they told me you had."

"And I tell you I haven't," said Peter emphatically, his customary good temper becoming ruffled under the Adjutant's cross-examination.

The Colonel intervened.

"Now, one moment. Let's straighten this out. Peter, you were at Brigade H.Q. this afternoon, weren't you ? "

"Yes, sir."

"Do you know that we 'phoned a message for you when you returned telling you to go to Divisional H.Q. at once, collect some orders and bring them here ? Did you get that message ? "

"No, sir. I didn't return to Brigade H.Q.," Peter explained. "I've been visiting the Battalion H.Q.s and I've brought back some fire tasks and the latest information."

"That settles it," said the Colonel gravely. "Something has gone very wrong here."

"Get me the Brigade Major at Div. H.Q. . . . Quick ! " shouted the Adjutant to the telephonist.

"Brigade Major on the 'phone, sir," said the operator a few seconds later, again removing his earphones.

"About those withdrawal orders for us," began the Adjutant. "We haven't received them. Our officer didn't come and fetch them. Whom did you give them to ? "

"One moment. I'll check up with our Intelligence Officer," replied the Brigade Major. "I wasn't there myself at the time. He handed them out." After a short interval he resumed :

"He says he handed the orders to an officer who said he was Captain Forbes."

"That's impossible," returned the Adjutant. "Captain Forbes is here now and says he hasn't been to Div. H.Q. What was this Captain Forbes of yours like?"

After a pause: "Medium height, dark, broad shoulders, wore battle-dress, carried a leather map case."

"Well, that fits in as far as it goes," agreed the Adjutant. "But the fact remains it wasn't Peter Forbes, for the simple reason that he was never there. This looks a damn serious matter."

"I'm well aware of that, old fellow."

"What's happened to the orders?"

"At a guess I should say that if they are not in the enemy's possession already, they'll be there very soon."

"Espionage, eh?"

"Or Fifth Column work. Possibly the wire has been tapped, and somebody has impersonated your officer."

"It sounds incredible."

"Not more so than a lot of other things that are happening just now," said the Brigade Major seriously. "You'll have to carry on with the orders, of course. Send the real Captain Forbes along straight away and I'll furnish him with a carbon copy. The best thing to do now is to lose no time in getting away. When you see the orders you'll realise that if they have fallen into enemy hands you may be in for a tough spell."

When Peter Forbes returned from Divisional H.Q. with a copy of the lost orders it needed not the Brigade Major's warning to impress on all concerned the dangers of the situation, presuming that the

original orders had been transmitted to the enemy.
Nothing was lacking in the way of valuable information.   Here was set down in black and white the time
for the Batteries to cease fire and withdraw, the new
area in which they were to come into action, the
route they were to follow and the time for coming
into action.

The Adjutant studied all these particulars with a
deepening frown.

"If anything has gone wrong," he observed with
foreboding to the Orderly Officer, "we can calculate
on getting it all ways, going, coming, and arriving."

He sat down beside the Colonel, and together they
compiled on message forms the detailed orders for the
withdrawal of the two Batteries, despatching them
forthwith to the Battery Commanders by a Don R.
Then R.H.Q. returned to its own packing-up.   The
Bren gunners were called in, the office equipment was
loaded into the vehicles, blankets were rolled up, and
the contents of the cook-house in the out-buildings
of the château piled into the mess wagon.   Last of all
the First Aid Room was cleared.   Splints, bandages,
slings, iodine and other medical stores were stowed
in panniers, and the stretchers strapped to the M.O.'s
truck.   Within an hour they were on their way down
the road to their new quarters.

The Adjutant had not to wait long before his
gloomy forebodings were realised.   Hardly had the
little column covered two miles when the ominous
drone of German bombers was heard.   Almost at the
same instant three Stukas dropped from the sky and
prepared to dive bomb them.   Everyone except the
Bren gunners leaped from the vehicles and took
cover in the ditches each side of the road.   For five
minutes the air was made hideous with the nerve-
racking screams of the diving Stukas, punctuated by

the explosions of the bombs. Alone in their truck the two Bren gunners poured burst after burst of machine-gun fire at the 'planes as they dived and climbed, without, however, achieving any success.

In the ditch the Adjutant found himself next to the Regimental Orderly Officer.

"No doubt, now, about what happened to those orders," he shouted in his ear. "This is pretty quick work. Peter Forbes's impersonator must possess a short-wave transmitter. After being in that château for two days without a bomb, I can't believe this attack is just a coincidence."

When the Stukas flew off, they emerged from the ditch to inspect the damage. Two men had been blown to pieces and the ration lorry was in flames.

"We've been lucky," commented the Adjutant. "We may go a bit hungry, but if that's our complete dose for to-day we have nothing to grumble about. Let's hope the Batteries come off no worse."

Leaving the ration lorry to burn itself out the column remounted and completed its journey to new headquarters without further incident. On their way, at a cross-roads outside a small village, they dropped the Second-in-Command, a Major, whose duty it was to await the arrival of the Batteries and go forward with the Troop Commanders to reconnoitre the gun positions in the new area.

It was quite dark when the Second-in-Command finally arrived at the farmhouse where new R.H.Q. had been established. He wore a very worried look.

"What's happened?" asked the Adjutant, apprehensively. "Anything wrong? Did the Batteries have a rough passage?"

"Not on the road," replied the Second-in-Command grimly. "Their packet was being kept for them till they arrived. D'you know, the whole of our area is

under shell fire already. Very heavy shell fire. The
Germans were actually plastering it before we arrived
to reconnoitre the Troop positions. They must have
known exactly where we were going, and prepared
the reception in advance. I've been dodging shell-
bursts most of the time. We fixed the positions under
a hell of a strafe, and when I departed the guns were
just moving up. God knows what will happen to
them. It's pretty suicidal, I can assure you. If
Division doesn't know the facts of the situation they
ought to be told."

The Adjutant nodded. " I'll see the Colonel about
it," he said.

As there had been no time to re-establish contact
with Division by 'phone it was necessary to send the
information by despatch rider. He returned in an
hour bringing fresh orders. The regiment was to
withdraw immediately to new positions ten miles back.

The Adjutant flicked the message-form with his
finger.

" Thank heaven it isn't a carbon copy this time,"
he said.

Then he despatched instructions to the Batteries to
pull out of their death trap.

Two days later, during a temporary halt in the
retirement of the British forces northwards, the
Adjutant ran up against his friend the Brigade Major
in a village street. It was the Adjutant's nature to
chafe under a mystery—even a minor one. He suffered
from an insatiable hunger for explanations. The
sight of the Brigade Major reminded him that on and
off for the past forty-eight hours he had been afflicted
by the craving keenly, and he welcomed the chance
to allay it.

" Did you ever hear any more about those orders
that went astray ? " he asked.

" What orders ? " replied the other. Already it was forgotten history to him.

The Adjutant recalled the circumstances.

" Ah, yes. I do remember now," said the Brigade Major, with the air of a man who had infinitely more important things occupying his mind.

" It might have been much worse for us than it was," continued the Adjutant, a trifle nettled. " I suppose you never discovered who intercepted the orders ? "

" My dear fellow, of course not. What chance have we of tracking down suspicious characters in this moving warfare, when we're here to-day and gone to-morrow. Unless you happen to catch a Fifth Columnist red-handed it's hopeless. That's how it is they are able to thrive so efficiently. As to your little affair we never even got as far as suspecting anybody. I presume some enemy agent impersonated your officer and took the orders. Whoever it was, I'd be pleased to meet him. But I'm certain I never shall."

" I see. It will remain a mystery," said the Adjutant, disappointed.

" One of many," remarked the Brigade Major, with an assenting nod.

A BRUSH WITH REFUGEES

VII—A Brush with Refugees

A WEEK after the German irruption into Belgium and
France, a battery of British artillery was halted in
a " hide " formed by a long avenue of trees bordering
a by-road midway between Ninove and Eyseringhen,
about fifteen miles from the battle-front over towards
Brussels. The Battery was part of a regiment
supporting an Infantry Brigade which had proceeded
forward to take up a defensive line just west of
Brussels. It was now late in the afternoon and the
Battery still awaited further orders where it was to
go into action. These they expected to arrive at any
moment from Regimental Headquarters which had
gone on some miles ahead.

The column had dismounted. On the grass bank
opposite their vehicles the gunners and drivers
squatted about in groups in the warm sunshine,
smoking and chatting, but mainly occupied in watching the never-ending procession of refugees hurrying
along the road in a westerly direction. Most of them
were pedestrians, little family groups of peasants,
pushing their household belongings before them in
hand-carts and wheelbarrows, the men attired in their
best black suits and bowler hats. Judged by their
clothes they might have been going to Sunday church
rather than fleeing from their homes before an

invader. But on their faces could be read their dumb
despair, the panic-stricken urge that drove them
forward dead-tired as they were. All the faces bore
the same fixed expression, those of the children as
well as the men and women. They paid little attention
to the soldiers sitting by the roadside. Occasionally,
without stopping, one of the men would ask:
" Tournai ? " and the soldiers would point down the
road, and say good-naturedly : " That's right, chum.
Keep straight on." Tournai was fifty miles distant,
on the French frontier. The soldiers did not understand that these questions were not so much inspired
by a desire for direction as by anxiety for an
assurance that the road to Tournai was still safe from
the Germans. The refugees had nowhere else to seek
for information. The Belgian civil authorities had
left them to fend for themselves.

At the head of the column the Battery Commander
sat by the roadside opposite his truck in conversation
with the three Troop Commanders. They, too,
watched with interest and pity the sad flow of
humanity before their eyes. In the Major's mind the
pity had, during the last half-hour, become less and
less predominant, not because he lacked compassion,
but on account of his own growing anxieties. The
more refugees that passed in front of him the more
acute these anxieties became.

A thin, undersized peasant, pushing an old
perambulator on which was tied a huge, bulging roll
of dirty bedding, tramped past. Behind trudged his
wife, a stout, middle-aged woman, dressed entirely in
black like a mourner. She had dragged up her blouse
from the waist, exposing a heavy breast at which she
suckled an infant as she walked along. A second
child, a beady-eyed little girl not more than four years
of age, had harnessed herself with a piece of rope to

the front of the perambulator, and plodded forward like a beast of burden.

"This is a side of war I never realised," said the youngest of the three Troop Commanders, averting his eyes. He felt it a matter of delicacy to avoid letting the little group round the perambulator perceive the sympathy with which he had observed them.

"Unless I'm very much mistaken we are going to realise it presently in a way we shan't relish," snapped the Major. "This is only a by-road. Yet the crowd has been getting thicker and thicker every five minutes. God knows what it'll be like on the main road. If there's any truth in this rumour that the Government have evacuated Brussels we'll find half the population of the city sweeping this way, to say nothing of all the fugitives from Louvain and Malines. The road will be choked. I wonder how the devil the Battery is going to get through when we do start moving."

He removed his tin-hat and glowered into the crown of it. The Major's temper well-matched his appearance which was exceptionally fiery. Short, stiff, very red hair covered his head like bristles on a brush. His eyebrows were of the same hot hue, and his eyelashes only a shade lighter. His neat, clipped moustache was, if anything, stiffer and more fiery than his hair. Added to which, his complexion looked as if it had been baked to a brick-red in a kiln. In build the Major was short and wiry, and his general resemblance to a watchful and aggressive Irish terrier could scarcely be missed.

"If the Germans calculated beforehand on this sort of thing happening, then they've got brains," he continued. "A mob such as I expect to find on the main road is worth a division to them in holding up our troops. I suppose it's the same all along the front. I hope those damned orders arrive before dark."

Another half an hour passed during which the Major's forebodings strengthened as the numbers on the by-road increased alarmingly. At last, to his intense relief, a Don R, from Regimental H.Q. came chug-chugging up the road, forcing a way for his motor-cycle through the middle of the refugees. The Major hastily snatched the message-form from the rider's hand, and studied it alone in conjunction with his map.

" Orders ! " he shouted down the column when he had finished.

All the officers, and the sergeants who were the Number Ones on the guns, hurried up to him with their maps.

" The Battery is going into action in the north-east portion of square 3667," he announced. " O.P. areas, small ring contour square 3766. Regimental zero line, 90 degrees . . ."

He informed them of the Wagon-Lines area, and the route to be taken.

" Pace of vehicles will be as fast as possible," he continued. " We have to be ready to open fire at 19.00 hours (seven p.m.). That gives us less than two hours, and we've got anything but a clear road. All vehicles nose to tail. We'll have to risk that. If not, we'll never get through the mob. Any questions ? . . . No ? . . . Then get mounted."

In a short while the column, nose to tail, was moving at a fair pace along the by-road, the Major in his truck at the head, followed by the Troop Commanders, and the reconnaissance party.

Their troubles began the instant they reached the junction with the main road that led from the direction of Brussels westward towards the French frontier. Not even the Major had anticipated things would be quite so bad. Brussels had been evacuated by the Government and a great exodus from the city was in progress. The entire width of the road was packed with a confused mass of refugees, all pressing on like a slow flood in the same direction. Thousands and thousands of them, as far as the eye could see. Compared with this the by-road was a desert. There it had principally been pedestrians. But on this main road the pedestrians were inextricably mixed up with every conceivable type of wheeled vehicle— motor-cars, ranging from luxurious limousines to old crocks that hadn't been outside a garage for years, taxicabs, push-cycles, motor-cycles, farm wagons, stacked high with household furniture, and with the clods from the fields still sticking to their wheels, contractors' lorries shared by four or five families, and covered vans with the addresses of Brussels trades- men on them. In addition innumerable hand-carts, barrows, and perambulators piled with personal belongings being pushed along by men, women and children.

Rich and poor, old and young, peasants and town- dwellers alike, went to compose this monstrous, seething throng of fugitives in which individual identities seemed to be swamped, and only the herd remained. All were being driven forward by the same impulse. In each the same blind instinct pre- dominated, the powerful instinct of self-preservation. There was something fearful, as well as pitiable, about this relentless eruption of human souls united into one desperate, unreasoning horde by a common terror.

Ordinary courtesies of life, little acts of kindness to strangers had disappeared. No one had time for them. All that mattered was to push, shove, force oneself to the best of one's powers in front of other people. A few yards gained by jostling someone else out of the way was a great prize. Men, women and children, on foot or on wheels, centred their entire thoughts in this struggle, which was carried on with a terrible unflagging persistency derived from panic. Just as the Battery reached the junction of the roads its further progress was barred by a farm cart, stacked high with the furniture of a household. A bed in which lay a bedridden old woman crowned the summit. The cart had come to a temporary halt and the single horse between the shafts lacked strength to start it in motion again. The animal strained and plunged about in the harness, its hoofs slipping on the concrete road. No one lifted a finger to help the old farmer who, with the sweat pouring down his forehead, vainly supplemented the horse's efforts with his own.

By the roadside, close to where the Major's truck came to a standstill, two peasants and a young woman bent over the body of their companion, an aged white-haired man who had collapsed from fatigue. He lay motionless with his eyes closed. Struggling with the concern at his condition depicted on the three faces was a vexed impatience with the author of this prolonged delay. The group made no attempt to disguise their feelings. So strong was the display of resentment expressed by the younger of the two men, that the Major could not forbear thinking : " I'll bet that fellow is wishing the old chap would die and have done with it."

At the other side of his truck a small girl screamed in terror. She had become separated from her parents, and the chances of finding them again in that vast, seething crowd were remote. A man picked her up and perched her on his shoulder. " Can you see them ? " he asked. After gazing around for a while the child sobbed " No." Without more ado the Good

Samaritan dumped her on to the road again and passed on. The tide swallowed her up, and the Major was not sorry when he could no longer hear her screams.

" Get down and give that fellow a hand or he'll stick there till the war's over," he said to his driver.

The driver jumped from the truck and proceeded to the assistance of the old farmer. Together they managed to start the wagon laden with the bedridden woman in motion again. Then the Battery moved slowly forward, forcing its way yard by yard through the confused mass of refugees, many of whom showed the strongest disinclination to yielding up the slightest share of the road to the troops. After a while, the Major, exasperated by this sullen reluctance to give the Battery passage, said :

" Drive straight at 'em. If they won't get out of the way, that's their look out."

But although this drastic measure bore some success with the pedestrians, it prevailed little against the lorries, carts, and wagons that incessantly endeavoured to pass one another, even if it meant monopolising the entire width of the road. As time went on the hold-ups became more and more frequent. Not the faintest semblance of traffic order, to say nothing of control, existed. Drivers drove their vehicles to right and left as they could, and as they would. The slightest gap was seized upon as a chance to pass some vehicle in front. To the Major, in a hurry, the chaos was maddening. Pedestrians followed in the wake of the slow-moving vehicles in huge droves. Cyclists, many of them Belgian gendarmes who had decided it was high time for them to relinquish their functions, threaded their way in and out of the throng, weaving crazy patterns from one side of the road to the other. Here and there little human eddies swirled round some overladen cart that had broken down and obstructed the passage.   In such cases the owners abandoned their goods and chattels forthwith and joined the army of walkers.   Women who had been seized with cramp sat by the roadside with their skirts drawn up while husbands massaged their naked legs and urged them to get on their feet again.   From somewhere in the crowd a cry of " Thief ! " went up. Nobody paid the slightest attention, least of all the gendarmes on bicycles, who seemed only too anxious to sink all trace of their former connection with authority and become submerged in the common lot. Like everyone else they were in the grip of a panic that swept all other considerations out of its path.

Though the Battery column started on its journey nose to tail, it soon failed to maintain this compact formation in the maelstrom that it found itself forced to struggle against.   Little by little the gaps between the vehicles caused by the continual hold-ups became wider.   After some time they were strung out for a distance of a couple of miles.   Each truck, gun-tractor and ammunition-trailer had to fight its own individual battle to make headway.   An hour of their precious time passed and they were still several miles from their destination.   The Major's temper had reached explosive point.   He glanced at his watch and swore loudly.   The Battery had been ordered to come into action at seven o'clock.   There wasn't the ghost of a chance of its doing so.

Whatever general sympathies he had felt to begin with for the refugees had long since evaporated.   His job was to bring his battery into action.   This undisciplined mob seemed to be doing all in its power to frustrate him.   He might have been carrying on a feud with them.   Every yard provided him with a fresh source of irritation.   The climax came when his truck was suddenly confronted by two white plough

horses yoked to a broad, heavily-laden farm wagon.
At their head, holding the reins, stood a giant of a
fellow in shirt sleeves, a Fleming, with a large florid
face and hair as red as the Major's own. He was
urging on the horses to pass another wagon in front,
and completely blocked the road. The Major choked
with fury.

" Pull in, there. . . . Pull in . . ." he shouted in
French.

The giant returned him a surly glance and took no
further notice.

" Did you hear what I said ? " yelled the Major.
" Get back where you came from and let us pass."

The other swore back at him in Flemish. With a
contemptuous gesture he flung out a huge hand as if
to brush the Major off the road. Behind the wagon
the Major could see a thick crowd massing, ready to
sweep forward as one man when the wagon moved.
He realised that something must be done quickly.

Jumping out of his truck he confronted the sullen
giant, who glared down at him with bitter animosity.
A sudden hatred towards this man filled the Major's
heart. Red-haired himself, he cherished an instinctive
dislike to red-haired men. And upon this one he was
just in the mood to concentrate all the exasperation
he had accumulated during the past hour. His blue
eye fixed themselves on his adversary in a cold anger.

" If you don't instantly back your horses, I'll do it
for you," he said.

" That remains to be seen," replied the other in
French. At the same time he repeated the insolent
wave of his hand.

The Major wasted no more words. He stepped
forward and grabbed the reins from the fellow's hand.
For a second the red-haired giant seemed dumb-
founded. Then, frantic at the prospect of losing the

few yards of the road he had hoped to gain, and perhaps more besides if his wagon were backed, he raised his whip and would have brought it down on the Major's head, if the latter had not shot up a hand and caught the thick wrist in an iron grip. They stood for a moment glaring at each other as only mortal enemies can, strangely disproportionate in bulk, the Major looking like a terrier about to fling himself at the throat of an infuriated bull.

Instead he suddenly hurled the fellow's wrist from his grasp. A new idea seized him during that moment when he stared deep into the Fleming's eyes. He divined there the absolute panic that held possession of the man. Sheer blind panic that rendered him completely impervious to reason or argument. Terror of the Germans had half-demented him. There was only one way to tackle him, and that was to instil into his mind a more powerful and immediate fear that would, for the time being, drive the other into abeyance.

With an unhurried deliberation that he hoped would not be without effect, the Major drew his revolver. He pulled back his sleeve and thrust his wrist-watch under the nose of the Fleming.

" If you haven't backed your wagon out of my way in one minute from now, I intend to shoot you," he said sternly.

For some seconds he watched the progress of the struggle that was being waged within the other's mind, the battle of contending terrors, and wondered what he should do if, after all, his device did not succeed. He knew, of course, that he would not shoot the fellow, though at the same time his hatred was so intense that he felt nothing would give him greater pleasure. As the watch ticked away, in order to speed up matters, he raised his revolver slowly till it pointed straight at the man's heart. The great, broad face of the refugee glistened with perspiration. He stared down at the revolver and his fleshy countenance took on a trapped expression. Breathing heavily, he shifted his eyes to meet the Major's, and read there only a cold implacable determination to carry out the threat. With one final look in which the token of his surrender was accompanied by a blaze of fury, he stepped back and commenced to drag the two white horses out of the Major's path. Revolver in hand, the Major followed him till the wagon had been backed for some distance, which in the congested state of the road was not a simple matter. The red-haired pair exchanged one parting glare of mutual enmity. Then the Major returned to his truck.

After this delay, which had been responsible for the loss of another invaluable five minutes, the Battery column moved slowly forward again. From now onwards the Major stood up in his truck, one hand on the windscreen and the other, still brandishing the revolver, waving the refugees aside whenever they impeded his passage. This manoeuvre achieved some effect. It checked the tendency of drivers to cut in, and the column progressed at a more even rate, if no faster, than before. Finally they reached a sunken road, where they were to turn off in the direction of the battery area. Some distance along this they halted while the Major and the reconnaissance party proceeded ahead to reconnoitre the Troop position.

It was now half-past seven. There existed no possibility of the Battery getting into action before eight-thirty, the earliest. The probability was that it would be nine o'clock. Leaving the Troop Commanders to lead the guns to the selected positions in adjacent fields and orchards, the Major drove off to R.H.Q. to interview the Colonel. He was still fuming with anger after his experiences on the road, and the fact that he fully anticipated a " rocket " from the C.O. for being behind time did not improve his temper.

" I'm terribly sorry I'm late, sir," he began. " We had the devil's own job getting through the refugees. The road was choked with them. I had to threaten them with my revolver or we shouldn't be here now. I'll have the Battery in action by eight-thirty, I hope. It may be a little later."

" We're not going into action," said the Colonel much to the Major's surprise. " We've got to go back. Fresh orders have just arrived. Apparently the infantry met with the same troubles on the road as you, and didn't arrive in time. The Germans are this side of Brussels by now."

" Then, because of those damn refugees we've all got to withdraw without a fight."

" That's the position," said the Colonel. " Here's your new area. Get the Battery moving as soon as possible."

The Major drove back to the Battery Command Post and despatched a Don R. to the Troop positions with orders not to come into action but to re-form in the road. An hour later, with dusk falling, they started for their new positions, travelling back the way they had come. This time progress was simpler. They were now journeying in the same direction as everybody else. Also, the number of refugees had appreciably diminished. The first frenzied rush was over. Besides which, in the last hour and a half the road had lost some of its attraction for the fugitives. German 'planes had paid attention to it. As the Battery column approached the junction of the main road with that leading to their former " hide," the signs of the severity of the attack became evident. The dead bodies of more than a score of civilians lay scattered on either side of the road, which was littered with the debris of wrecked vehicles. Bomb craters pitted the bordering fields, now dotted with little groups of refugees who, dreading a new attack, had forsaken the highway and pressed on their way in the twilight, still dazed by the horrors they had survived.

Led by the Major in his truck, the Battery turned down the almost deserted by-road, but after a hundred yards it was pulled up by a farm wagon that had been smashed by a bomb explosion. Two white horses lay dead in front of it. Even in the fading light the Major recognised them at once. They belonged to the obstreperous red-haired giant who had held up the Battery on the main road earlier in the day.

" Get a dozen men from the tractors and clear the road as quickly as possible," he said to his driver.

He himself also descended and strode across to examine the shattered vehicle. The explosion had blown both wagon and contents to pieces. Two of the wheels were missing entirely. One of the white horses had been disembowelled and the stench in the neighbourhood was already overpowering. He could see no trace of his old adversary.

While the troops were engaged in clearing the wreckage the Major lit a cigarette and strolled down the road to escape the smell of dead horse. He had not proceeded far when he heard groans. In a shallow ditch by the roadside lay the giant Fleming. He had been terribly wounded in the side by a bomb splinter, and his broad, florid face was now grey and twisted with pain. As the Major bent over him the man's eyes opened.

" You ! " he gasped, with a flash of recognition. " That is good. . . . You will shoot me now. . . . For the love of Jesus. . . . I suffer atrociously. . . . Shoot me . . . for the love of Jesus. . . ."

The eager, imploring look that accompanied these words, forced out like difficult breaths between the spasms of the man's agonies, sent a shudder through the Major. Only the most dreadful sufferings could prompt such a frenzied prayer. It was quite obvious that the poor devil's case was hopeless. Swift death would be a mercy for him.

Again the wounded man clamoured frantically in husky, broken sentences to be shot. The dread of being left there to suffer haunted his eyes.

" I'll do it," decided the Major, after a third agonised appeal, and, to the sufferer's great relief, he commenced to draw his revolver from the holster.

As he did so their eyes met again, and suddenly the Major was aware of undergoing a change. Very vividly he recalled the scene on the main road of a few hours before. He recalled the intense hatred towards this man that had filled his heart. He recalled with what pleasure he could have shot him then. And now. . . . No, he couldn't do it now. Some powerful force seemed to be holding him back. If the man had been a complete stranger, yes. It would have been unpleasant, but he could have tackled the job. But with this fellow it was different. Only a few hours previously he had passionately desired to kill him. He could not forget that. Yes, it was that which made all the difference now. It made it impossible . . . utterly impossible. The mere idea revolted him. Some deep instinct within him forbade it.

He replaced the revolver in the holster. On seeing the action the expression on the wounded man's face changed first to utter dismay and then to rage. Between his spasms of agony he heaped curses on the Major in a mixture of French and Flemish. The Major did not understand all the words, but he could follow the drift.

" He believes I won't do it because I'm his enemy. and enjoy letting him suffer," he said to himself. " My God ! I can't for the life of me shoot him. And he'll die thinking that of me."

He began to retrace his steps towards the Battery column, with the intention of asking one of the Troop Commanders to put the fellow out of his misery.

" No. I can't do that," he reflected, coming to a pause when out of earshot of the groans. " It's a nasty job to ask anyone to undertake. They'll wonder why I didn't do it myself. And I can't explain. I hardly know, myself. . . . I ought to have done it, I suppose. Yet I couldn't. . . . Perhaps it's merely a matter of lacking the moral courage. . . . Still, the fact remains I hated that fellow. And I think I hate him still. . . . If I put a bullet in him I'd never be quite sure I'd just acted out of pity. . . . Poor devil ! "

" Road clear, sir," announced a voice out of the semi-darkness at his elbow.

" Thank God for that," exclaimed the Major, glad to have other claims on his attention. " Get mounted."

In a few minutes the Battery Column had passed out of sight.

THE DUMP AT BETHUNE

VIII—The Dump at Bethune

" HERE ! Take a squint at that," said the Second-in-Command, as the Lieutenant-Quartermaster entered R.H.Q., about seven in the evening.

He tossed over the ammunition returns of the regiment's two batteries which had just been brought up by a Don R. from their " hide " on the outskirts of Laventie. They were the routine returns, made out daily, indicating the quantity of shells and charges expended during the past twenty-four hours, and the total amount of ammunition of various kinds the batteries still had in hand.

Giving a quick glance at the forms, the burly, red-faced Lieutenant-Quartermaster made a noise halfway between a snort of derision and a contemptuous laugh.

" This won't do," he said.

" I should think not," agreed the Second-in-Command, emphatically.

The Lieutenant-Quartermaster studied the returns once more, and made a few mental calculations.

" Smoke, armour-piercing . . . Plenty of that junk, of course. It's H.E. and charges they're down to the uppers on. This figure gives each Troop only another fifty rounds. Say a dozen rounds a gun. What the devil have they been doing with the stuff ? Eating it ? . . . A dozen rounds a gun . . . Barely enough for a respectable hot-up."

" It's more serious than that," observed the Second-in-Command. " We're going into action to-morrow outside Ypres."

" Are we, by God . . ."

" Orders just down from Division. If we have to put down big concentrations of fire on various areas, those supplies will be exhausted in twenty minutes. You've got to get hold of some H.E. and charges immediately. Lots of it. Where's the nearest dump ? "

The Lieutenant-Quartermaster, whose job it was to liaison with the R.A.S.C. Supply Column and to look after all regimental supplies—food for men as well as for guns—remained silent for a moment.

" I don't know," he confessed. " Paterson will be coming along any minute now, with the rations. He'll know."

" Good ! " exclaimed the Second-in-Command. " It's his job, anyhow. We can get him busy on it at once."

Within five minutes Second-Lieutenant Paterson of the R.A.S.C. Supply Column, whose headquarters were fifteen miles away at Erquinghem, drove up to R.H.Q. in his little 10-h.p. four-seater, camouflaged Austin. He announced his arrival with a flourish on the hooter, and disappeared inside the office. He was a dark, thin-faced, sharp-featured young man with a pair of shrewd eyes and an ironic twist to his mouth.

" Good evening, Major," he said. " I've managed to snatch some rations for you. The lorry's just behind. No bread, though. I doubt if you'll be seeing any more. The Germans have captured the bakeries at the base. Sorry . . . You'll have to eat cake, as Marie Antoinette told the starving peasants."

" Bread doesn't matter a damn," interrupted the

Lieutenant-Quartermaster. " We're short of something more important than that."

" What ? "

" Ammunition. We're going into action to-morrow,
and we haven't enough to knock a sparrow off a tree.
Do you know where you can lay your hands on any
25-pounder H.E. and charges ? Not to-morrow, but
now."

The young subaltern knitted his brows over his
shrewd eyes for a moment or two. Most of the big
ammunition dumps had been planted out in fields
by the roadside. Stacks of shells of all calibres,
camouflaged with branches, at intervals of a quarter
of a mile, and extending in some cases, for a distance
of six miles. As the British retreat developed the
bulk of these were blown up to prevent them falling
into enemy hands. The R.A.S.C. officer knew all
about this.

" Bethune," he said, after reflection. " There's a
smallish dump there."

" Bethune ? " echoed the Second-in-Command.
" That won't do, my boy."

" Why not ? "

' Because the Germans are probably there by now
When we crossed the canal midday at La Bassée
they were pressing us pretty hard. And between us
there was only a light covering force. No more than
a few Bren-guns and a company or two of infantry.
Bethune is only ten miles lower down the canal, so
it's fair bet the Germans have occupied the town.
Mind you, I've not heard anything official. It's just
common sense. No, I can't say I like the sound of
Bethune. Isn't there another dump somewhere ? "

" I don't recall one in the area," said the subaltern
after a pause. " There is, or was, the big one near
Lille. But that's in enemy hands."

" Anything in the Ypres neighbourhood ? "

" Perhaps.   But I don't know of it."

" We've got to get that H.E. somehow, from some-where," the Lieutenant-Quartermaster broke in, im-patiently.

" Couldn't you borrow a bit from another regi-ment ? " suggested the R.A.S.C. officer.

The Lieutenant-Quartermaster regarded him with a pitying expression.

" My dear fellow," he said gently. " Have you ever tried to borrow water from a thirsty man in a desert ?   Have you ever tried to borrow ten pounds from a fellow that's saving up hard to get married ? Borrow ? . . .   You might as well try to borrow the moon.   Everybody wants all the ammunition they've got for themselves . . .   So, where are we now ? "

" Back at Bethune," said the subaltern, cheerfully.

" And I still don't like the idea," the Second-in-Command demurred. " I can't believe the Germans aren't there."

" Perhaps Captain Thompson has received some information by now," said the R.A.S.C. officer. " I'll scoot back to my headquarters and ask him to let you know what can be done."

" As quickly as possible."

" Yes.   As soon as we have had a good think about it."

" Think as good as you like, if it amuses you," interposed   the   Lieutenant-Quartermaster, grimly. " But don't lose sight of the fact that you've bloody well got to get that ammunition to-night, whatever happens."

The ration lorry was just rumbling into sight when Paterson rejoined his car.   The Lieutenant-Quarter-master followed him out with the necessary requisition for the ammunition.   Paterson looked at the figures.

" This lot means we'll require eight 3-ton lorries
to load it," he said, dubiously.

" Well, what about that ? " demanded the Lieutenant-Quartermaster aggressively.

" Oh, nothing," laughed the R.A.S.C. officer, step-
ping into his car.   " Except that it provides Captain
Thompson and myself with more food for good
thought."

The Lieutenant-Quartermaster watched him depart,
wondering what the devil he was getting at.

It wasn't till dusk was falling, at about eight
o'clock, that he was enlightened. A Don R. arrived
at R.H.Q. with a message to the Adjutant from
Captain Thompson, the officer in charge of the R.A.S.C.
Supply Column. The Adjutant summoned the Lieutenant-Quartermaster.

" Send down to the batteries," he said, " and tell
each of them to supply two 3-ton lorries with drivers
and four men armed with rifles, all to be outside R.H.Q.
at 20.45 hours (quarter to nine)."

" What's it for ? "

" The Supply Column want them for this ammunition hunt.   Most of their own lorries are away getting
rations and other supplies. They've only four avail-
able. Here's Thompson's message. It looks as though
it's going to be a tricky job."

Captain Thompson's message was brief and to the
point. Bethune was the only possible place where
they could hope to obtain ammunition at such short
notice.   There were conflicting reports about the
position of the enemy, but all agreed that the British
had cleared out, and if the Germans hadn't entered
the town already, they were on the outskirts and might
be expected any moment. It would be foolish to
disguise the fact that the enterprise was attended by
grave risk.   It might fail completely. Would the

contingent of lorries from the regiment meet Mr.
Paterson at the road junction south of Estaires, map
reference 346–871, at 21.30 hours (half-past nine)
by which time it would be quite dark.

"I see there all the ingredients for a nasty mess,"
continued the Adjutant, uneasily.

The Lieutenant-Quartermaster nodded.

"It can't be helped," he said. "We've got to
have the shells. If Bethune is the only chance, they
must risk it."

He departed to make arrangements for the despatch
of the four lorries.

*   *   *   *   *

Fifteen miles away, at the headquarters of the
Supply Column at Erquinghem, Captain Thompson and
Second-Lieutenant Paterson sat over a meal in a
bare room in a wrecked farmhouse close to the main
road. In the darkening courtyard outside stood
Paterson's 10 h.p. Austin and the four lorries that
were to take part in the raid on the Bethune dump.

On the table between the two officers a hurricane
lamp burned smokily by the side of a china jug the
dimensions of a small ewer, in which hot and very
dark brown tea was steaming. The jug, primrose
yellow in colour and adorned with a flowery design,
lent an odd note of domesticity to the rough-and
ready character of the meal.

"Have another steak," invited the Captain, hacking
off a slice of bully-beef with his jack-knife and dumping
it in his companion's mess tin. "You'll probably feel
hungry before the night's over. Nothing like a big
meal before a big job. Eat first, and then we'll dis-
cuss details."

For the next ten minutes they spoke little, concentrating on the bully beef, biscuits, and tinned fruit

salad which they washed down with mugs of strong
sweet tea.

" There's no need for me to warn you that you've
got to be damn careful over this business," said the
Captain finally, lighting a cigarette. " My latest
information is that the Germans haven't crossed the
canal. It may be wrong. Even if it isn't, that's not
to say they aren't in Bethune the other side of the
canal. In which case small parties may have crossed."

" You bet I'll be careful," replied Paterson, draining
a mug of tea. " Careful as a cat burglar. It's damned
lucky that dump is on this side of the canal. Otherwise we couldn't have done anything, now all the
bridges are blown up."

" What N.C.O. are you taking ? "

" Sergeant Lambert."

" Let's have him in, then, and we'll get down
to it."

Paterson went to the doorway and called : " Sergeant Lambert." In a few moments the sergeant
appeared, a man of portly mien in the early forties.
He contrived to invest the most trivial things he did
with an air of importance by the impressive deliberation of his manner.

" Help yourself to a mug of tea, sergeant," said the
Captain.

Sergeant Lambert produced an excellent imitation
of a scientist in a laboratory carefully pouring into a
test-tube some rare distillation   When the mug was
half-full he suddenly stopped, his glance fixed on the
outside of the jug

" A most striking coincidence, sir," he exclaimed,
portentously

" Oh, what ? "

" This pattern, sir   Exactly identical with the one
on the jug and wash-basin in our bedroom at home."

The Captain laughed.

" Makes you wish you were back there, I suppose ? "

" Not at the moment, sir," replied the sergeant, after due consideration. " But there's no saying it won't when we get to Bethune."

" I trust things will turn out better than that," said the Captain, hastily. " Get your maps, and we'll run over the route."

The maps were spread out on the table, and he proceeded :

" After picking up the artillery lorries you'll go straight down the main road from Estaires to Bethune. When you get to the outskirts continue straight on till you come to an estaminet at a cross-roads. You can't miss it, even in the dark, because it's painted white. Turn off right here and carry on for about four hundred yards down the road. On the left there is a small disused factory. In the main shed of the building you'll find the ammunition."

" If it hasn't been already blown up," interposed Paterson.

" Yes, there's always that possibility," the Captain admitted. " If so, it's a journey wasted . . . Now what about men, Paterson. How many do you think you'll need ? "

" The fewer the better," Paterson replied, promptly. " Not one more than is necessary. This is merely a trip to collar a few shells . . . if we can. Either we get the stuff without a fight, or not at all. I'm hoping we shan't run into trouble. If we do we may not come back. So why waste men . . ."

The Captain turned things over in his mind for a while.

" Sergeant Lambert, you'll ride in the first lorry with ten men," he said finally. " Take a Bren-gun and an anti-tank rifle. See that the rest of the men are armed with rifles. Each of the lorries behind will carry a driver and one other man, both armed with rifles. If you should be surprised on the road, sacrifice the first vehicle by pulling it across to block the way. Dismount the men, take cover, and hold off the attack till the remainder of the vehicles have had time to turn and get away . . . Other way round, of course, coming back. That clear ? "

" Yes, sir," answered the sergeant, stolidly.

" You, Paterson," continued the Captain, " with your driver, and two men in the back of your car, will go on at least half a mile ahead of the column to reconnoitre. Halt the column at the top of the road leading to the dump while you go forward and make a reconnaissance of the area. Make certain the enemy aren't the other side of the factory. When you're sure it's safe, pull in and start loading. You ought not to take more than an hour and a half. I'll leave it to you to post sentries and mount the Bren-gun and the anti-tank rifle in the best positions. Any questions ? "

" No. It all sounds like child's play," said the subaltern, ironically.

The Captain turned once more towards Sergeant Lambert.

" It's up to you, sergeant," he said earnestly, " to impress on the men the absolute necessity for quiet. No talking at all. Any orders must be passed down the column in whispers. And definitely, no smoking. Make as little noise as possible. Don't accelerate too much. And don't rev. up when changing gear. When you're on the road keep the vehicles close together to avoid losing touch in the dark. Remember you can't be too careful on a job like this. See that the men realise it."

" I will, sir," said the sergeant.

He rose to go, and Paterson followed him into the dark courtyard.

" Pick only the best and most reliable men, sergeant," he said. " Especially the drivers. Be prepared to move off in ten minutes."

He re-entered the house, collected his equipment, torch and revolver, swallowed another mug of tea, and walked out again to where little groups of men clustered round the four lorries in the courtyard waiting for the start.

" Everything ready, sir," announced Sergeant Lambert.

" Right ! Get them mounted, and we'll be off."

He was about to proceed to his car when from one of the groups came a violent sneeze, followed immediately by a second. Paterson strode across.

" Who sneezed ? " he asked.

" I did, sir," replied one of the men.

" Why ? "

" I couldn't help myself, sir. I've got a touch of hay fever."

" Sergeant Lambert," called Paterson, " fall-out that man and get a substitute. Anybody else here with a sneeze, cough, or other noise that he can't keep under control ? If so, let him fall-out, too. All of you had better understand that a good deep breath is about the safety limit in noises on this trip."

No one availed himself of the invitation, so Paterson walked off to his car. The Captain was standing by.

" You've a fine dark night for it," he said encouragingly. " There's hardly a star. Well, *au revoir*, old fellow, and good luck ! I've ordered a Don R. to travel in one of the lorries with his machine. When you turn off the road on the return journey to convey

the stuff to the batteries send him back to me so
that I know you are all right. I shall be damned
anxious till I hear. Good luck . . ."

They shook hands. The little column started into
motion. In the darkness the Captain watched till
it disappeared down the road. He felt far from
confident of ever seeing it again.

When Paterson and his vehicles reached the
rendezvous, the four lorries from the batteries had not
arrived. They switched off their engines and waited.
Soon the other contingent could be heard coming along
the road. In the utter silence the noise of their engines
sounded far too uncompromising to suit the requirements of the R.A.S.C. Officer.

" Too much low gear about that," he said to Sergeant
Lambert. " You could hear them for miles. They'll
have to change up."

The lorries arrived at the rendezvous. A sergeant
jumped out and reported to Paterson.

"All right . . . But your vehicles are making far
too much row, sergeant."

He impressed upon the sergeant the urgent necessity
of cutting down noise to a minimum, strictly forbade
talking and repeated over to him Captain Thompson's
instructions. The artillery lorries tacked themselves
on to the rear of the others and they moved off in the
direction of Bethune, Paterson in his Austin leading
the way.

They travelled along the pavé road at a steady
pace for some miles. As the Captain had observed,
it was a pitch-black night. The day had been hot
and the air was still warm and breathless. A film of
cloud had spread over the sky at sunset. There was
no moon, and only an occasional star shone in the dark
heavens. A faint ground mist hovered over the flat
fields on either side of the road.

After proceeding for some while Paterson experienced more and more the unpleasant sensation that danger was creeping nearer and nearer towards him. Usually, at all times of the day and night, small parties of British—stragglers, a despatch rider, a vehicle or two —were to be encountered on the roads in the wake of the retreating army. But to-night the way back south to Bethune was completely deserted. The very last straggler seemed to have drifted northwards long ago. The column had it completely to themselves. Paterson considered that these signs of isolation could only indicate one thing. The advance of the enemy had been speedier than they had expected. As the car hummed along he found himself continually wondering how many more yards he would be able to cover before running slap-up against the Germans. In readiness he drew his revolver, not to make a useless fight against odds, but to fire a few shots out of the window to warn the column and give them time to escape.

At last a straggle of deserted houses by the road-side apprised him that they were approaching the outskirts of Bethune. He dropped to a crawl and kept an eye wide open for the estaminet. Even painted white it would not be too easy to spot on such a black night. Ah, there it was. He pulled up, detected no sign of life about the place, and ordered one of the men in his car to wait at the spot to ensure that the column did not make any mistake and pass it. Then he continued down the side road on the right and very soon reached the factory. The sheds stood a little way back from the road through a gateway. It was a relief to discover they were not a heap of ruins. That meant the dump hadn't been blown up. After getting so far with the job, he hated the idea of having to return empty-handed.

He parked his car and, revolver in hand, crept across the yard to the main shed, halting every now and then to listen. But he heard no sound. Cautiously raising the flat iron bar that fastened the doors of the shed, he entered and shone his torch. There was the ammunition all right. Piled up in stacks, each about six feet high and twenty feet long, with narrow corridors between. A dump of yellow six-inch H.E. shells with plugs in them and the fuse-boxes nearby occupied the front part of the shed. That wasn't what he was after. A quick look round and on the far side his eye alighted on some stacks of long, shallow tin boxes, painted a dark green. By the light of his torch he read the yellow lettering on the boxes : " 25-POUNDER H.E." Next to them stood the deeper boxes containing the charges.

" That's the stuff," he muttered with satisfaction. " And now to get it away."

He emerged from the shed, leaving the door open, and made a quick reconnaissance of the remainder of the factory buildings, and its immediate neighbourhood. Nothing occurred to alarm him. The place was as silent as the grave. So he hastened back on foot to the estaminet where the lorries were drawn up like a mass of deep shadow by the roadside. To complete his reconnaissance he turned up the road leading to the canal, in the direction of the enemy, and scouted along for several hundred yards. The unbroken silence struck him as uncanny, much though it reassured him. He padded up and down the streets in the vicinity, hearing not a sound. All the houses were completely empty. Not so much as a dog barked. Not the rustle of a breeze. The absolute stillness of the air intensified the silence. Once he fancied he could detect a muffled rumble in the distance, away on the other side of the canal, which might be

the noise of enemy tanks.   But he had been listening
for some time so intently he could hardly trust his
ears by now.   All sorts of queer murmurings and
echoings seemed to fill them.

He made his way back to the estaminet.

"All clear, for the present," he said to Sergeant
Lambert.   "Start loading.   And don't waste any
time."

The lorries crawled down the side road to the factory.
Paterson retained three men and a bombadier and
planted them in the estaminet with the Bren gun and
the anti-tank rifle so that they could command the
street leading from the canal, this being the most
likely way of approach for any enemy parties that
might cross the canal thereabouts.   Having attended
to this, he returned to the factory.   The loading had
commenced, and as he drew near he was staggered
by the noise made by the tin shell-boxes scraping
together as the men slid them into the lorries.   In
his keyed-up state the din seemed appalling.

"God Almighty!   They'll bring the whole beehive
down on us," was his first impression.   "We'll never
get away with this."

Then he realised that the job couldn't be done on
tiptoe.

"I'm getting a bit nervy, I suppose," he said to
himself.   "I expect I'm hearing more than is
justified."

He completed his precautions by placing four look-
outs round the factory with instructions that if they
saw anything suspicious they were to run back and
give him word.   On no account were they to shout
an alarm.

He watched the loading for a while, but found it
impossible to reconcile himself to the inevitable noise.
Each scrape and shuffle seemed to reverberate through

the night air with the clang of a steam-hammer. Loud
enough to be heard by any Germans on the other side
of the canal.   He knew this was simply a freak of his
imagination.   But it kept him all the time in a stew
of apprehension that he found a bit trying.   As he
couldn't alter matters he walked back down the
road towards the estaminet to remove himself from
earshot.

At the estaminet he poked his head through the
empty window frame.

" Seen anything, bombardier ? " he asked.

" No, sir.   Heard nothing neither."

" Good.   Keep your eyes peeled."

Once more he crept round the black, deserted
streets near the canal bank, still fancying he could
hear the row they were kicking up at the dump, and
half expecting every moment to run into an enemy
patrol.   But the streets remained as dead and silent
as before.   He returned to the dump.   The shadowy
figures of the men, laden with the shell-boxes each
weighing over a hundred pounds, lumbered to and
from between the shed and the lorries.   Sergeant
Lambert stood by to see they were not overloaded.
Two and a half layers of boxes on the bottom of each
vehicle was about the maximum.

" What progress, sergeant ? " inquired the R.A.S.C.
officer.

" Three lorries loaded, sir."

" That all ?   It's too damn slow," exclaimed
Paterson impatiently.   " At that rate we'll be here
till daybreak.   For God's sake, hurry the men up.
Every minute matters.   So far we've been lucky.
But it can't last for ever."

" Shall I send the vehicles off one by one ? " suggested the sergeant.

" No.   They might be caught by a small party on

the road," Paterson replied. " We stand a better chance of getting through if we keep together."

The R.A.S.C. officer went across to the shed and put in a spell of loading with the men. It helped him to forget the noise they were making. Another half an hour passed without any alarm. He paid a second visit to the estaminet. Everything remained quiet there. No sign of life had come from the direction of the canal. When he returned to the dump they had just commenced loading the last lorry. He was in a fever of impatience now to get the job finished. Each minute added to the suspense. A curious feeling took hold of him—an indefinable impression that things were waking up. Very much as if dawn were about to break, although it was still some hours off. He sensed the vague stirrings in the atmosphere, in spite of the fact that nothing seemed to have changed.

Suddenly, as if in confirmation of his instinct, a German success rocket streaked up against the black sky and burst into a white ball over Bethune.

" That's our notice to quit, damn it," he muttered. " Even if it isn't too late already."

He was about to cut the job short with the intention of getting away with the ammunition they had already loaded, when Sergeant Lambert emerged from the darkness.

" All ready to move, sir," he whispered.

" Then move, in heaven's name," said Paterson. " It's high time we were going. See that rocket. It'll be a miracle if we get clear."

He jumped in his car and drove down to the estaminet, where he alighted and stood by the roadside counting the laden vehicles as they came round the corner. One—two—three—four—five—six——

He got no further. Without warning the Bren gun in the estaminet behind him suddenly opened fire.

156

He swung round and peered down the road leading to the canal. As he did so red flashes of rifle fire stabbed the darkness about four hundred yards away, and bullets sang in the air. One grazed the side of his tin hat and the impact caused him to stagger.

" Blast it ! . . . We're going to be pipped after all," he thought as he recovered his balance.

He yelled to the lorries to drive on at top speed. Never mind the noise now. . . . The seventh came round the corner, lurching and swaying, and hurled itself down the road after the others. The eighth, according to the pre-arranged plan, swung across and blocked the road. Sergeant Lambert and the ten men leaped out and crouched behind it, firing back at the red flashes in the direction of the canal. The Bren gun continued its short bursts of fire, five or six shots at a time. Paterson, having seen the vehicles disappear, darted into the estaminet.

" Hold 'em up, bombardier," he shouted. " Whatever happens, we must give the lorries time to get clear."

The bombardier nodded and despatched another spatter of bullets. For a minute or two the exchange of fire proceeded vigorously. Then, surprisingly enough, almost as suddenly as they had appeared, the red flashes down the road ceased. The Bren gun continued to spray the spot, but there was no reply. In another minute dead silence had descended on the street again. For half a minute they waited breathlessly for a further attack. But it never came.

" Must have been a patrol. They've withdrawn," said the R.A.S.C. officer. " We'll make it yet. Quick ! Into the lorry, everybody."

He ran out, shouting to Sergeant Lambert to back the lorry straight on the road again. While the driver did so the men pitched themselves into it. In a short

while it was tearing along at top speed to catch up
with the rest of the column.

For a quarter of a mile or so Paterson followed it
in his car. Then, as there seemed no sign of pursuit,
he went forward, overtook the other vehicles near the
old rendezvous south of Estaires, and without further
incident conducted them with their treasure to the
battery positions at Laventie.

*   *   *   *   *

It was a quarter to one in the morning when the
R.A.S.C. officer once more showed up at his headquarters at Erquinghem. He looked very tired, and
his sharp features were sharper than ever. He
walked into the room in the ruined farmhouse where
he had eaten with Captain Thompson only a few hours
before. It seemed to him he had been away much
longer than that. Yet there was his mess-tin still
on the table, with the juice of fruit salad in it, just
as he had left it. The hurricane lamp was still smoking
beside the yellow jug that had reminded Sergeant
Lambert so forcibly of his bedroom at home. He supposed it must be the reaction after the excitements at
Bethune that made all these things seem strange to
him.

The Captain, who was sitting at the table, looked
up as he entered. He had already learned from the
Don R. whom Paterson had sent back that the job
had been carried out.

" Congratulations, old fellow," he said warmly. " A
nice piece of work. You pinched that stuff from under
their very noses. Our pal the Lieutenant-Quartermaster ought to appreciate that bit of gun-fodder.
You'd make a good crook. I don't mind confessing
now that it wouldn't have surprised me if you'd never
come back. What happened ? "

" Oh, nothing to speak of," said Paterson, the ironic twist of his mouth more evident than ever. " The stuff was there ready waiting for us. All we had to do was to load up and bring it away."

" And the little skirmish ? "

" That ? Oh, just a bit of rifle fire to keep us from falling asleep."

The Captain regarded him sympathetically as he dropped into a chair.

" You do look a bit weary," he said. " You want a bit of shut-eye. Well, now's your chance. Have half an hour before you go to collect those rations from Bailleul."

" Sure you can spare it ? " said the R.A.S.C. sub-altern with a mirthless laugh.

" Spare what ? "

" The whole half-hour."

AT THE MENIN GATE

IX—At the Menin Gate

THE events of the night of May —th, 1940, would never have possessed their peculiar significance in the eyes of Captain John Ware, R.A., but for an evening in October, 1928.

On that evening John Ware, a thirteen-year-old boy in a school cap, stood by the side of his father before the Menin Gate leading into Ypres. It was after seven o'clock, and the drizzle of rain that had been falling all day still persisted. Young John Ware was tired, chilled and bored. Hungry, too. It seemed ages since he had last eaten. And the next meal showed no symptom of approach. Not even the chance of a grenadine at a café brightened the immediate future. His father, apparently, had forgotten the existence of such a thing as food. John gave himself up, with melancholy resignation, to starvation.

John and his father were staying at Ostend, and John Ware, senior, was fulfilling desires he had cherished passionately for nearly ten years. He had hired a Belgian chauffeur to drive them on a tour of the battlefields of Ypres. Year by year, ever since the end of the war, his longing to make a pilgrimage to all the hallowed spots in this tragic corner of Belgium, once so painfully familiar to him, grew in

strength. Now that his first opportunity had come
he seized on it like a tiger. Young John wondered
why his father, usually so particular, neglected the
elementary precautions of lunch and tea. He did not
realise that John Ware, senior, was feeding himself
to the full on the feast of memories provided for him
by Poperinghe, Toc House, Hill 60, Passchendaele,
Zonnebeke, Hell Fire Corner and a host of other places
that were merely queer names to his offspring. John
Ware, senior, had no time to be hungry.

But young John found it thin fare for a growing
boy. As the hours passed he grew less and less interested in his father's unchecked flow of sentimental
reminiscence. At last it became difficult to pay any
attention at all. He tried to conceal his boredom,
and his impatience to return to Ostend. He did not
want to hurt his father's feelings But he wished he
hadn't come. He couldn't pump up the continual
enthusiasm expected of him. To him these old battle
sites looked very unimpressive. Just like any other
bare dreary fields in the rain There was nothing he
could see to get excited about. . . .

His father, of course, was seeing labyrinths of
trenches in which grim, mud-stained, khaki figures (of
whom he was one) crouched under ferocious barrages.
He revelled in the bath of diverse emotions evoked
by his memories. Descending the slope of Hill 60,
young John tripped over some rusty barbed wire,
a relic of the old entrenchments, still half-buried in
the soil. The result was a badly grazed knee and a
long tear in a new pair of trousers. Had the latter
misfortune happened to young John in the school
playground back in England, his father would have
expressed unpleasant annoyance. But now, he
thought it a great joke.

" Like father, like son," he laughed, clapping

young John on the back. " I got my first blighty
on Hill 60. Only it was a bit more than a hole in
the pants."

He reserved the visit to the Menin Gate till the
last. The grand tit-bit rounding off a memorable
day. Having deposited them in front of it, the
Belgian chauffeur retired with a newspaper to the
interior of his taxi in a fit of the sulks. His patriotic
interest in the tour had expired as soon as the model
Belgian trenches at Nieuport and Dixmude had been
explored. Which was very early on. Also, he was
bitterly incensed because John's father, by aid of a
sandwich or two, had foiled all attempts to induce
them to lunch at the Ypres restaurant for which he
was a tout on commission. He now strongly sus-
pected John's father of meditating further treachery
by returning to Ostend without even dining at Ypres.
The chauffeur made no attempt to conceal his disgust
at the whole affair. Young John's sympathies lay,
secretly, with the chauffeur.

Father and son stood in the drizzle on the flat
bridge over the canal. In front of them rose the great
white stone arch of the Memorial, surmounted by the
shaggy-maned sculptured British lion couchant.

" There's the old animal ! " exclaimed John's father,
surveying it with another thrill of emotion. " Still
keeping watch on the Menin Road."

" Looks half asleep to me," ventured young
John.

His father chuckled. " That's where the Boche
went wrong in 1914," he replied. " They found him
wide awake enough by the time he'd finished with
them. They won't be in a hurry to make that
mistake again."

The evening was so dismally wet and chilly that
few loiterers were about. When they passed under

the central arch into the lofty hall they had it almost
to themselves.

"Ah! There they are," said John's father, in a
hushed tone, as his eye alighted on the long columns
of names, carved in thin capital letters on the stone
of the walls.

He took off his hat in salute to the dead. Young
John copied him, and thought what a draughty place
it was.

"Sixty thousand names there," his father went on.
"Just names, now. All of them in unknown graves.
But for luck I might have been on that wall. Better
men than I ever was are."

He walked over to one of the slabs and began
reading aloud the names, one by one. Young John
was aghast. Surely his father did not intend going
through the whole sixty thousand. It would occupy
all night. The thought plunged him into despair.

But it did not prove so bad as all that. After a
while John's father began to pick out here and there
from the alphabetical lists names he thought he knew.

"Here, look," he said, pointing to one. "The
first time I went over the top that chap was next to
me. We kept together all day. It was his first go,
too. Both of us scared to death. But neither of us
got a scratch. . . . Last ever seen of him was at
Passchendaele. He was drowning in twelve feet of
mud in a shell crater. . . . I'm glad I wasn't there
to see it."

"Can I put my cap on?" said young John. "I'm
feeling terribly cold."

"All right," replied his father. But he still kept
his own hat in his hand.

After that they walked round the Memorial several
times, John's father feasting his eyes upon it from
different vantage points, the bridge, the bastion, and

166

the ramparts. He seemed unable to tear himself away. Once he did raise young John's hopes.

"Not feeling hungry, are you?" he inquired suddenly. "Lucky we had a good breakfast to start the day with."

"I could do with a grenadine," young John replied, with heroic moderation.

"Oh, that can wait," said his father, and once more they passed under the arch into the Hall of Names.

"D'you know why this is the grandest memorial in the world?" John Ware, senior, exclaimed, with a sudden burst of fervour. "Because it means: 'Never again!'"

"Never again what?" inquired young John.

"Never again those years of blood and agony we had to undergo. All those fellows on the walls gave their lives that their sons and their sons' sons should be able to live their lives in peace and security. Out there in the Salient lie buried a quarter of a million more, who died in the same Cause. By God! . . . It was hard to do, but we did it. And that's the message of the Menin Gate to the future. . . . So long as one stone of it stands. . . . 'Never again' . . ."

Young John began to feel quite uncomfortable in the presence of such a display of emotion from his usually reserved and correct father. It was like over-hearing someone saying his prayers.

After a few moments' silence his father consulted his watch.

"Are we going now?" asked young John hope-fully.

"Not just yet. I'm waiting for something."

"What is it?"

"You'll see," said his father mysteriously.

Darkness was now closing in rapidly, and the streets

were empty. They had the Menin Gate to themselves except for a Belgian errand boy, about the same age as John, who lolled with his back against his bicycle in the main archway. He, too, seemed to be waiting for something.

Eight o'clock chimed from a neighbouring church. Five minutes later John Ware, senior, again looked at his watch.

" Late," he muttered.

Then four elderly, rather shabbily dressed men in overcoats drifted into view from the Ypres side of the Gate. Young John took them for belated work-men on their way home. Two wore bowler hats, the others caps.

Much to John's surprise this shuffling group halted opposite where he and his father stood just within the arch, sheltered from the rain. They formed into a straggly line, their faces turned towards the direction of the Menin Road, and produced from beneath their overcoats four gleaming bugles. They solemnly re-moved their hats, put the bugles to their lips and, rather quaveringly, blew the " Last Post."

Young John glanced up at his father to see what he thought about this queer business. But John Ware, senior, appeared hardly conscious of his son's presence. He stood stiff at attention, gazing through the arch-way with a far-away look into the night shades gathering over what to him would always be the Ypres Salient. His eyes seemed to be watering. Young John noticed this, too, but charitably attributed it to the keen wind.

When the last plaintive strains had died away, the four men shook the spittle from the mouthpieces of the bugles, replaced them under their overcoats, and stole off as unostentatiously as they had arrived. The Belgian errand boy mounted his cycle and disappeared.

John's father emerged from his trance.

" Who were those men ? " inquired young John.

" Members of the Ypres fire brigade," replied his father. " Every evening, winter and summer, they blow the Last Post at the Menin Gate. It's ' Good night ' to all the brave fellows who sleep in the Salient. They'll never be forgotten. Nor the grand job they did. . . . The men who made the world safe for the likes of you, John. . . . Now we'd better think about getting back to Ostend."

" Can I have a grenadine before we start ? " asked young John.

" Oh, wait till you get back to the hotel," his father suggested.

The white mass of the Menin Gate faded behind them in the darkness as the taxi sped through Ypres. It was destined to fade out from the orbit of young John Ware for a matter of twelve years.

II

Towards the end of a hot, close afternoon, Captain John Ware of the 777th Field Regiment, R.A., and his Battery Commander, drove their trucks into the town of Ypres. Their Battery, retreating towards Dunkirk, had just come into action midway between Ypres and Poperinghe, and they were in search of a suitable Observation Post from which John, the O.P. officer, could direct its fire. They hoped to be able to find one somewhere on the easterly side of the town, looking over in the direction of Menin.

It was a ruinous, dangerous Ypres they entered.
Days of vicious, incessant air attacks had left their
mark upon the town, and, in addition, the Germans
were now shelling it vigorously from their positions
on the far side of the ·canal. Every now and then
John heard a shell burst, and another doomed building
tumbled to the ground with a roar like a cataract.
The skeleton walls of tall houses that had already
been bombed had a nasty habit of collapsing without
warning, blocking the road with piles of debris. Here
and there, fires raged so fiercely that the streets were
impassable. John, following a few yards behind the
Major's truck, found himself continually making
detours. So their progress was slow, and it was
further hampered by hastily improvised barriers,
largely consisting of heaped-up doors, wrecked cars,
and household furniture—which the British troops
had erected across the main thoroughfares to stop
the armoured vehicles of the enemy. Just after
negotiating the slit through one of these barricades
they were held up by a military policeman.

" What's the trouble now ? " snapped the Major.

" When approaching the next cross-roads, get over
as quickly as possible," was the reply.

" Why ? "

" Sniper busy, sir. We can't locate him. . . . Fifth
Columnist . . . they're doing it all over the town. So
look out."

The Major conveyed the warning to his companion.
They raced safely across the danger zone without
knowing whether they had attracted the sniper's
attention or not. Passing the Cloth Hall, now in
process of becoming a ruin again for the second time
in twenty-six years, they finally parked their cars in
a side street some three hundred yards from the Menin
Gate, and proceeded forward on foot.

Now they could hear, in addition to the whine of the shells overhead, the sharp rattle of machine-gun and rifle fire echoing from across the canal where the British troops were still holding up the German advance. An ambulance was drawn up outside a house before which, tied to a paling, floated a dirty white flag marked with the Red Cross. The front rooms had been transformed into a temporary infantry first-aid post, and a small group of very tired walking wounded from the battle area, with bandaged heads and arms, stood by the doorway waiting to enter as soon as the ambulance finished emptying its stretcher cases.

" I bet they've had a hell of a time," said the Major. " Ever see men on their feet looking so done in ? "

Captain John Ware did not answer. His attention was engaged elsewhere. They had suddenly come in sight of the Menin Gate. And at that instant, out of the tomb of memory, there rose the picture of himself as a schoolboy, cold and hungry, standing by his father's side in the rain, listening to four shabby men sounding the Last Post in the twilight. It was all so vivid and so surprising, that he came to a momentary halt. The episode had completely faded from his mind for years. He couldn't remember how far back it was since he had last given it a thought. And here it was, sharply pictured as if it had happened only yesterday. At the same time he noted that the Gate seemed to have shrunk in size, and become very much dirtier.

The Major noticed John staring rather hard in front of him.

" Never seen the Menin Gate before ? " he asked.

" Oh, yes," replied John. " My father dragged me here once when I was a kid. I hated it. The old man had—probably still has—a rather oppressive

reverence for it. Thought more of it than St. Paul's
and Westminster Abbey rolled into one."

" Not architecturally, I hope."

" Good Lord, no ! Symbolically. He regarded the
Menin Gate as a symbol that the world had said
good-bye for ever to war. I can remember distinctly
his words, almost on this very spot : ' So long as one
stone of it stands ... Never again ' ... Meaning there'd
never be another Great War. He believed it, too.
Like a religion."

The Major laughed. He was only thirty-five years
old himself, and a trifle cynical towards the lofty
aspirations of his predecessors in khaki.

" Well, his religion's busted, good and proper," he
said. " The Menin Gate's a has-been as a symbol of
anything. Unless it's the folly of being sure of anything good in this wicked world. But heaps of those
1914–18 veterans were tarred with the same brush.
They flattered themselves they'd made war obsolete.
And here we are."

By now they reached the entrance to the central
arch. Within, surrounded by the names of the
sixty thousand graveless dead, an anti-tank gun
manned by three gunners was in action.

" In a million years the old man could never have
dreamed that possible," John murmured.

" Nor this," exclaimed the Major, who had been
keeping his reconnoitring eye busy.

" What ? "

" The Menin Gate as your O.P."

" Sounds an idea," John nodded. " I'll get up and
see what is to be seen."

He climbed to the top of the Memorial and crept
along, sheltered by the parapet, to where the British
lion couchant still maintained its monumental watch
on the Menin Road. Cautiously he raised his head

and shoulders and peered over. Below him the flat bridge over the canal on which his father had stood years before in rapt admiration of the imposing façade of the Gate, still remained intact, though ready to be blown sky-high when the British troops on the other side were withdrawn. A few slightly wounded men were trickling across, and a Don R. flashed like a streak through the arch in the direction of the Menin Road. John raised his binoculars to examine his battery zone. But he had no time to see anything. A sudden burst of machine-gun fire rang out. Bullets hummed round his ears. Chips from the stonework of the Memorial flew in all directions. He ducked behind the parapet. Another sharp burst of fire followed, and another.

He made a hurried descent back to the Major.

" No good," he said. " It's under heavy machine-gun fire. Not a chance of observing."

" We'll try that church back on the right," suggested the Major.

They retraced their steps through some side-streets, mounted to the top of the church tower, and studied the distance through their glasses.

" Not very satisfactory," was the Major's verdict. " There's a large section on the left of the zone that you can't see at all."

Scarcely had he spoken when a rifle bullet slapped against the edge of the tower close to them. Almost immediately others whistled over their heads. They dropped out of sight like one man. Bullets continued to sing around.

" Damn it all ! . . . We're being fired at from the town," exclaimed John in disgust.

" I'm not so sure," replied the Major. " But wherever it's coming from, it's damned unhealthy. In any case, this place is no good for an O.P. Let's clear out."

They crawled off the tower in safety. Back in the street they made their way along the ramparts of Ypres. Detachments of British troops lined the canal on this side, dug into shallow trenches and occupying houses along the bank from which they kept up an intermittent fire on the tiny figures of the German infantry who, at intervals, became visible in the distance, slowly working their way forward towards the canal.

Nothing in the nature of a suitable O.P. presented itself. At length the Major glanced at his watch.

" Time I was getting back to R.H.Q., or I'll be late for the conference," he said. " I'll have to leave you to do the best you can."

After he had departed, John continued his search, walking back along the ramparts towards the Menin Gate. At last he spotted a tallish house, standing a little way back from the canal, that looked to have possibilities. The door was wide open. He stepped inside.

" Fire ! . . ." shouted a voice from above.

The surprise took him aback. Before he recovered another voice said : " Through, sir." He laughed at his scare. The well-known ritual. The house was already functioning as an O.P.

Upstairs he discovered two other gunner officers established in an empty top room, with their telephonists squatting on the floor.

" What, another ? " was the boisterous greeting he received. " We'll have the entire Royal Regiment rolling up before long."

" D'you mind if I butt in ? " asked John.

" The more the merrier, my dear chap. Bring a friend and complete the bridge four," replied the younger of the two captains. " What are you ? "

" The 777th."

174

" That's the stuff. Twenty-five-pounders. . . . Like me. Our pal here belongs to the bow-and-arrow department. In other words, he's amusing himself with a battery of eighteen-pounders."

" Make no mistake," retorted the other captain. " The eighteen-pounder's a damn useful little gun. We can fire before you're loaded."

Having satisfied himself that the O.P. provided a good view of his zone, John went off to collect his truck and his wireless operator. An N.C.O. in charge of signals had accompanied them into Ypres on a motor-cycle. John despatched him back to the Battery to guide and supervise a wire-laying party up to the O.P.

" Get through to the Battery," he told the wireless operator, when they drew up outside the house.

But the operator failed to establish contact.

" I can't get them, sir," he said, after trying for some time. " They've gone off. There seems to be a lot of interference."

" Blast. . . . I don't want to sit about doing nothing till the wire's laid. Fix up a remote control, and let me know the instant you can get through."

Meanwhile John settled down to the job of drawing a panorama of the zone, identifying the features of the landscape from his map, and checking up on some of the doubtful ones by reference to his companions. This took time. On finishing he paid another visit to his truck downstairs. The operator was still vainly endeavouring to connect with the Battery. John rejoined the other O.P. officers, chafing under the delay that was holding up his shoot.

The eighteen-pounder officer, who had been sweeping the front with his binoculars on the look out for a fresh target, suddenly uttered an exclamation of astonishment.

" Good Lord ! Look at that," he cried. " Four degrees left of the canal bridge . . . a thousand yards . . . just to the right of that small wood. D'you see it ? Or am I dreaming ? "

John took a squint through his glasses in the direction given. What he saw amazed him, too. There in the distance was a German horse-artillery battery, of all things, galloping into action in approved Aldershot Tattoo style. He could not resist the thrill of this stirring spectacle.

" What a grand sight ! Good old hairies ! " he exclaimed at the sight of the horses.

" Fine, aren't they ? " agreed the eighteen-pounder officer with enthusiasm. " Sometimes wish we had 'em still. Pure sentiment, of course. . . . Well, I'm sorry for the hairies, but I'm going to have a crack at that battery."

John assisted him to work out the switch, range, and angle of sight of this dream target, all the time cursing the bad luck that kept him out of touch with his own Battery at such a juncture. The other O.P. officer continued his task of shelling enemy concentrations behind a village over towards Zonnebeke.

The eighteen-pounder officer 'phoned down the orders to his battery. " Fire ! " he shouted.

" Through, sir. . . . Shot . . ." announced the telephonist a few moments later, and the two O.P. officers looked in for the shell burst. John, with the naked eye, in case it fell outside the field of vision of the other's binoculars.

" More thirty minutes . . . 6,400 . . ." came the correction.

" Through, sir. . . Shot . . ."

Again : " Less ten minutes . . . 6,800 . . ."

" Through, sir. . . . Shot . . ."

After ranging, the eighteen-pounder officer ordered

five rounds gunfire. The shells began to burst so close that their smoke obscured the target. One seemed to plump slap in the centre of the battery. Through their binoculars the observers could see little figures of men darting here and there in confusion. Then, gun teams with limbers galloped round from the side of the wood to withdraw the guns. Before this could be achieved one gun team received a direct hit. The ground became a welter of struggling horses and men, out of which, eventually, one small human figure alone detached itself and staggered away through the smoke.

" Yes. Give me the eighteen-pounder all the time," chortled the O.P. in high glee, when the excitement was all over.

" Give me any gun," groaned John, utterly fed up by his enforced inactivity.

He endured it for another twenty minutes. Then the arrival of the sergeant with the wire and a tele-phonist, made him happy. Afterwards, there was no cause to complain of the dearth of targets. All along the canal the German pressure increased hourly. At one or two places on the flanks they succeeded in forcing a crossing. Their tanks came into action, and kept the triple O.P. busy. Likewise the concentrations of their mechanised infantry, which were flung in ever-increasing numbers into the long, grim struggle for the town. Gradually, in face of overwhelming odds, the screen of British infantry began to withdraw to the Ypres side of the canal, where they clung to their positions tenaciously, despite the heavy and ceaseless machine-gun fire, and the shelling from trench mortars.

Dusk was descending on the battle when John's telephonist summoned him to the 'phone. It was the Major.

" Pack up at once and come in," he said. " The Battery is going back."

" We shan't be so long in following you, from the look of things," said John's companions when he announced the news.

On arriving at the Battery position John was surprised to find that although preparations for withdrawal were in an advanced stage, his own Troop had not even started to hook-in their guns. The Major enlightened him.

" The Battery is withdrawing to Oostuleteren," he explained. " All except your Troop. That stays behind to support the rearguard. You, yourself, will proceed to the hamlet of L——, for liaison with the infantry. According to my information you'll find Battalion H.Q. of the 9th Loamshires there."

" Impossible," cried John. " The place must be in the hands of the Germans by now. They crossed the canal close to L—— an hour ago."

" Those are the orders. You've got to go there," replied the Major with a shrug. " You won't need a wire. Have your guns laid on these S O S lines before you start. Directly the infantry need assistance fire a red Very light from their H.Q. The Troop will then open fire on the S O S. lines. For the first three minutes, intense. . . . Next quarter of an hour, normal. Bring your Troop out of action at 3 a.m. and rejoin the Battery at Oostuleteren. All clear ? "

John nodded, and departed to find his Gun Position Officer, to whom he gave the map co-ordinates of the S O S lines, and instructions to keep a sharp look out for the red Very light. Then, accompanied by a wireless operator, he once more started off for Ypres. The journey was far more uncomfortable than his daylight one. More fires than ever were blazing. The German shelling had intensified and heavy

178

explosions constantly shook the streets. Red flashes from the bursting shells lit up the darkness intermittently on either side of him. It was suicidal to proceed at more than a crawl through the chaos of the streets. Even then his truck continually came into collision with unexpected heaps of rubble and broken glass in the roadways. Snipers from roofs and windows fired at everything that passed. One bullet whizzed through the rear of the truck, narrowly missing the wireless operator's head.

After leaving the southern outskirts of the town, John drove for some miles without encountering a soul. There was more quietness now. But he found it by no means a reassuring calm. He had fully expected to run into some signs of our infantry along the road. Their complete absence strengthened his conviction that L—— must have been occupied by the enemy. In which case, at very best, he was heading straight for a German prisoner-of-war camp. The prospect weighed heavily on his spirits, and the farther he went the more his anxiety increased. Once or twice he stopped, thinking he might have taken the wrong road in the dark. But on checking up from his map he could discover no mistake.

At last a few scattered houses appeared in sight. He pulled up, parked the truck in the thick shadow of some trees, and cautiously made his way towards them on foot. After a while he heard voices just ahead of him in the darkness. A sudden feeling of panic seized him. He drew his revolver and shouted : " Are you British ? "

" Yes," came the reply, and he thanked heaven for it.

It was a group of eight very weary and dusty infantrymen belonging to the 9th Loamshires.

" Is there an officer about ? " he asked.

" Over in the cottage. I'll take you," one of the men replied.

The door of the cottage had disappeared. John stepped straight from the darkness into a bare room dimly lit by a hurricane lamp. An infantry lieutenant and a subaltern reclined in a couple of chairs with their feet on a table. Another subaltern lay in a heavy slumber on the floor. The faces of all three were covered with several days' growth of beard, and their battle-dress was stained and dirty.

The two officers at the table stared glassily at John from red-rimmed eyes.

" Are you the 9th Loamshires ? " he asked.

" Yes," replied the lieutenant huskily. " What do you want ? "

" I'm gunner liaison officer," replied John.

He was quite unprepared for the reception accorded to this piece of information. For a moment the infantry officers stared at one another, and then broke into harsh, derisive laughter.

" By God ! . . . a visitor from the outside world," cried the subaltern. " Liaison ! . . . that's rich ! . . ."

" Don't mind us," the lieutenant hastened to say, seeing John's expression stiffen. " We don't mean to be discourteous. . . . D'you know, we haven't had any sleep for three days. It's been one long fight. We're pretty well all in. The lot of us. . . . I mean those who are left. And now we don't care a damn. . . ."

The long strain of battle that was so marked upon their faces, had brought them to the verge of desperation. Any hope of coming out of their ordeal alive had apparently vanished. It was obvious they lived now with the sole grim intention of making their exit as objectionable to the enemy as possible.

" Is this Battalion H.Q. ? " asked John.

Again the subaltern went off into a fit of mirthless laughter.

"That's damn good," he cried. "My dear chap, I don't know why you are here, and I don't care. But let me tell you where you are. This is Company H.Q. of the most forward Company of the battalion. It's a very hot spot, indeed. And it's going to become hotter, blast it ! . . . If you want to see a bit of fighting, just hang around here. Not that I recommend it."

"Can you tell me where I can find Battalion H.Q. ? " John inquired.

"Have a drink before you go," said the lieutenant, producing a bottle of whisky.

"No, thanks."

"Go on, have one. Have two . . . have three . . ." urged the subaltern. "You'll need it before you've finished liaison with us."

Again John refused as politely as possible. They poured themselves out a couple of drinks.

"Well, here's to . . . here's to. . . . What the devil is there left to drink to ? " muttered the lieutenant gloomily.

"Here's to whisky . . ." exclaimed the subaltern defiantly, swallowing his drink at a gulp.

Then the lieutenant, making a tremendous effort to overcome his fatigue and attend to John's business, shouted :

"Orderly. . . . Take this officer along to Battalion Headquarters."

John experienced intense relief on quitting this atmosphere of hopelessness. Not much imagination was needed to guess the ordeal these men had undergone. It was plain to him they had given themselves up for dead. Nothing mattered any more to them.

" We're here to be killed. . . ." That summed up their attitude. The stark fatalism of it chilled John.

" And they're probably right," he could not prevent himself from thinking.

On reaching his truck he relegated the driver to the rear with the wireless operator, and occupied the driving seat himself, the guide at his side. After proceeding in pitch darkness for nearly a mile they came to a Bren-gun carrier blazing by the roadside. John's suspicions were at once aroused.

" Are you sure this is the right road ? " he asked the guide.

The man hesitated. " Can't say I remember that carrier, sir," he admitted.

" We've got to make certain," said John, pulling the truck up sharply. " God knows what we may be heading for."

He jumped out and walked down the road for about thirty yards. Suddenly he found himself face to face with the canal. He dashed back to the truck.

" You damn fool ! " he shouted furiously at the guide. " You've led us straight into the canal— almost."

They retraced their way till they struck a road branching off to the left. This proved to be the right one. About three-quarters of a mile farther on Battalion H.Q. of the 9th Loamshires was established in the cellar of a farmhouse in the middle of some fields.

Immediately John entered he sensed a tension in the atmosphere that reminded him of the forward Company H.Q. The Colonel, stoutish in build, sat at a table, his attention riveted on the map spread out before him. He was sweating profusely, and had divested himself of his web equipment, which hung on a nail behind him. The Second-in-Command leaned over his shoulder, expounding his views on the emergencies of the situation, and jabbing his forefinger at different spots on the map to emphasise them. Opposite, a young subaltern, fighting to keep awake, watched them in a sort of hypnotised, staring silence. Orderlies came and went continually with messages. Upon all faces intense fatigue and anxiety had stamped their mark. From outside echoed bursts of machine-gun fire in the not-so-far distance, with now and then the explosion of a shell.

The tired, harassed Colonel was in a devil of a temper. John introduced himself and received a grunt.

" What lines are your guns laid on ? " the C.O. snapped, without bothering to raise his head.

John explained, conscious that the Colonel was barely listening. It was evident he was too preoccupied with the dispositions of his troops to think about anything else at the moment. The scanty information he was receiving left him very much in the dark as to what might be going to happen.

" Where do you expect the attack, sir ? " John inquired.

" How the hell do I know," was the reply.

John went on to inform him of his instructions to send up a red Very light when assistance was needed.

" Assistance ! . . ." cried the Colonel in an outburst of impatience. " I've half a battalion left. . . . The assistance we want is a brigade of infantry, not a Very light. We've been wanting them for the last twenty-four hours."

Ignoring John, he returned, fuming to his map. After a minute or so he cooled down.

" If I've been a bit short, forget it," he said, with a show of apology. " Make yourself comfortable. I expect we'll be glad of your help before the night's out."

John propped himself up on some straw in a corner of the cellar. No one took any further notice of him. The critical nature of their situation monopolised all their moments, and left no room for mere politenesses. As time progressed the night battle continued to flare up and die down in spasms. Firing broke out in some unexpected quarter and the dog-tired subaltern was despatched on a hurried mission. John gathered that the Colonel's chief concern was the danger of attack from the rear. But no definite information was forthcoming. So mixed up was the fighting in the darkness, he was hardly sure of the where-abouts of his own thinned forces, let alone the enemy's.

Two o'clock came with the suspense still as oppressive as ever. The time had arrived for John to think about taking his departure.'

" I must be going now, sir," he told the Colonel. " I have to take my Troop out of action by three o'clock."

" Very well," replied the Colonel abruptly, and took no more notice.

" Have you a red Very light ? "

" Yes," volunteered the Adjutant.

" Fire it if you should need our help while I'm on my way back," said John. " I'm sorry I can't stay longer."

He was on the point of leaving the cellar when a company runner entered with a message for the Colonel. After reading it the Colonel handed it to the Second-in-Command, at the same time regarding John for the first time that night with a definite display of interest.

" If you want to be of real assistance," he said, " here's your chance. That message is to the effect that the enemy are concentrating heavily in the area

of the Menin Gate. Put your guns on them as soon
as you can."

The Menin Gate . . . For the second time in a
few hours Captain John Ware's mind performed a
flash-back of twelve years. Once again the irony of
it brought him up with a jerk. The Colonel noticed
the odd expression that appeared momentarily on
his face. Misunderstanding it, he said with heavy
sarcasm :

" You have heard of the Menin Gate, I suppose ? "

" I'll get back to the Troop instantly, and shell
them till three o'clock," was John's response.

" That's all we want," said the Colonel. " We're
going back ourselves at half-past."

While the truck bore him back through the night
to the Troop position, John, with the aid of his torch,
worked out from the map the switch, angle of sight
and range of the new target, to avoid loss of time.
In measuring the angle he took the Menin Gate itself
as the centre of the target area, drawing the catgut
of his protractor exactly across the spot. By the
time he arrived his calculations were complete.

" Quick . . . Urgent target . . ." he shouted to
the Gun Position Officer as he jumped from the truck.

" What ? "

" Big enemy concentrations in the Menin Gate area.
Do a quick check up on these figures. I'll do the
shoot. It's only till three o'clock."

The guns were switched from their S O S lines on
to the new target.

" Ten rounds gunfire . . . One-five minutes . . .
Irregular intervals . . ." John ordered.

" Fire ! . . ."

The roar of the guns provided the unequivocal
background for his mixed reflections.

" For all I know," he said to himself with a grim

humour, " one of these shells may give the old man's idol its knock-out."

And then, with a sudden qualm of conscience :

" If I ever do get home again, I don't think I'll be in a great hurry to tell him about this."

RACE WON BY DEFAULT

X—RACE WON BY DEFAULT

EVEN with death dropping on them from the skies at fairly regular intervals of an hour or so, men found time to be bored on Dunkirk beach.

On a warm morning in the beginning of June two of the most pronounced sufferers from this complaint were Dave Williams and Eddie Harding, despatch riders in the 777th Field Regiment R.A. A flock of early German bombers had just finished unloading their stuff, and were disappearing to the accompaniment of scattered rifle fire from a few optimists on the beach. The two Don R.'s, who had flung themselves flat when the attack opened, rose in easy stages to their feet, spitting grains of sand from their lips. They stood a second or two in silence, gazing, not at the receding 'planes, but at the receding sea. It was without a ripple. Not even a sparkle helped to lend it animation. A morning haze hung over it, deadening it to a dull grey. And the smoke pall from the fires of Dunkirk pressed heavily upon the haze.

" I never did have much use for the seaside so early in the year," remarked Eddie Harding in strong disapproval of the monotonous aspect of the sunless waters.

" Nor me, either," assented his companion. " August's the month."

189

With a final disparaging glance they turned their backs on the scene and began to stroll aimlessly along the beach. Here and there other small parties of soldiers were behaving likewise, trying to relieve the tedium of the waiting hours before evacuation. Daylight embarkation had by this time been abandoned. In face of the incessant attacks by the German dive-bombers the risks were too great to be justified. So the troops were advised to make themselves scarce during the daytime and muster on the beaches after nightfall for the boats. They concealed themselves in dug-outs in the dunes, and in underground cellars in Dunkirk itself, sleeping away as much of the time as possible. Nevertheless, more men than might be expected preferred to chance stopping a bomb- or shell-splinter rather than endure the utter boredom bred by squatting hour after hour in a hole in the sand with nothing to do.

The two Don R.'s had arrived on the beach the evening before, after their regiment had blown up its guns outside Dunkirk. They effectually removed their Norton machines beyond possible reach of the enemy by plunging them into the deep water in the dock, braving the terrific heat of the blazing oil tanks in order to make a good job of it. Then they queued up in the sea for a boat. But luck was against them. When dawn came, much to their disgust they found themselves faced with a whole day in which to kick their heels about in the sand before their chance came again.

Though the pair were always together, and preferred each other's society to that of anyone else, it would be incorrect to describe them as bosom friends. They were, in fact, bosom rivals. Their attraction for one another depended entirely on the professional interests they possessed in common. Motor-cycling was the strong link that united them. It was a bitter-sweet companionship. Each was jealous of the other's pretensions to prestige as a rider, and betrayed it in a sort of amused tolerance, seasoned all the time with a variety of sarcastic comment. Both were modest young fellows in everything except their prowess as riders, the only difference between them being that whereas Eddie Harding's was a quiet conceit, Dave Williams made no bones about exhibiting his unblushingly to the world.

" I was a bloody fool to get rid of my machine last night," Dave said suddenly with conviction, as they wandered up the beach.

" Why ? " asked Eddie.

" If I had it here, I could do some riding on the sands."

" What for ? To show off ? "

" Or to teach you a few tricks."

" Not on that machine," said Eddie firmly. " You couldn't have rode that bike any more. When you drowned it you did an act of mercy."

" What do you mean ? "

" Wasn't it a mercy to put it out of its misery ? That engine was burned right out. I had my eye on it for some time. It was just about finished. You talk a lot about your riding . . . Yours isn't riding at all . . . crashing along like you do . . . It's murder. You'd kill the best machine ever built without knowing you were doing it. Real riding isn't pulling a machine's guts out. Real riding's nursing it."

" Like you did at Marœuil," retorted Dave, scornfully. " Nursed it so much it fell asleep on the road. And you with it. It'd done you a bit of good to hear what the Adjutant said."

" You don't know what he said. But I'll listen."

" He said, next time he wanted a message delivered quickly he'd employ a Don R."

" Meaning you, I suppose," sneered Eddie.

Exchanging similar pleasantries, they gradually climbed from the beach to the dunes. By a sort of instinct their footsteps were drawn to one of those tracts close to Malo-les-Bains that had become graveyards for all the miscellaneous types of army vehicles wrecked and abandoned by the units of the B.E.F. as their retreat came to a termination on the beach. Around this doleful morgue prowled motor-mechanics and driver-mechanics of artillery, tank and infantry regiments, busy examining the different vehicles with a professional interest to discover how they had been put out of action. A ruling passion takes a lot of suppressing, even when it is no more violent than a slavish devotion to carburettors and sparking plugs. So it was with these specialists. Bereft of their beloved machines they felt at a loose end. Such was their hunger for the companionship of the internal combustion engine that even the constant threat of the German bombers could not prevent them from gratifying it. In these stark cemeteries of dismantled trucks and lorries they became happy again. Their boredom vanished. They spent long hours tinkering about with bits and pieces of broken machinery, patching up something here, something there, transferring unbroken parts from one engine to another that had need of them, until at last they had completed a repair, and put a battered wreck in working order again. The crowning moment came when they pressed the self-starter and heard the engine throb. Then, having indulged in a minute or two of pardonable pride in their own skill, they would smash the engine to pieces again and wander off till they found another problem in re-conditioning worthy of their expert attention. Dunkirk roared in flames behind them. The dive bombers came and went. But it made no difference to these devotees. They flattened out when the bombs dropped, and rose again to resume their joyous labours the instant the sky was clear.

Being devotees in their own restricted sphere, the spirits of the two despatch riders lightened as they grasped the nature of these activities in progress around them. It was not long before Dave Williams pounced on a half-buried Norton motor-cycle, shook it free from sand and examined it with an expert eye.

" Now, Eddie. Watch me bring it back to life again," he exclaimed when he had finished his inspection of the damage. The dynamo was missing, but otherwise there wasn't much wrong beyond little things like bent brackets, which could soon be straightened or hammered out.

" If I can find a dynamo knocking about, I've got a bike," Dave added, in a tone of such aggressive confidence that Eddie decided at once not to be relegated to the position of a mere spectator of his rival's skill.

He wandered off looking for another abandoned Norton, upon which he could exert his own abilities as a mechanic. He found one eventually, which had been rendered useless by the removal of the sparking plug from the cylinder. A big hole gaped in the side of the petrol tank. While Dave prowled round the graveyard in search of a dynamo, Eddie did the same on the look-out for a Norton petrol tank without a hole, and a sparking plug. It took them some time, but they found their spares and a few tools at last, and settled down to do the repairs, side by side.

Dave finished first.

"Now for the juice," he said, setting out on another tour of the graveyard. Just as Eddie put the last touches to his repairs, he returned with an old petrol tin which he had filled by draining into it the last dregs of petrol left in the tanks of wrecked vehicles. Dave poured half into his own tank, and handed the remainder to Eddie. Then he gave the starter a couple of kicks. The engine burst into life.

"Didn't I tell you I'd have a bike?" Dave shouted in triumph. "There isn't much in the way of repairs to a motor-cycle that beats this little fellow . . . How are you getting on, Eddie? Ruined it for life yet?"

Eddie replied with a kick at his starter. The response was a faint splutter, and after a few seconds the engine died away. He kicked again with the same result. Dave, whose engine was behaving perfectly, grinned at his companion in derision.

"What's wrong, despatch rider?" he said. "Want any help? Don't worry. There'll be an A.A. scout along presently."

His sarcasm spurred Eddie to a particularly vicious kick. As the engine coughed hesitatingly he tried to coax it into song by twisting the accelerator grip with his hand. It continued to splutter in fits and starts, threatening every moment to expire, and Eddie only contrived to keep it going by skilful turns of the twist-grip.

"I always said I could deliver a message by the time you'd started your bike," continued Dave, enjoying the situation immensely. "Pity there isn't a garage handy, so you could get a good mechanic to give it an overhaul. Probably only wants a slight adjustment . . . Well, I'm going down to the beach. Why don't you come along and see an exhibition of riding? Better than wasting your time here."

"I'd be wasting my time watching you," replied Eddie emphatically, still adroitly manipulating the twist-grip. "Exhibition . . . That's just what it would be! You're suffering from that bronze medal you picked up at that phoney cross-country trial. And I'll tell you something else. A fellow doesn't become a dirt-track rider by riding up and down the Old Kent Road with a New Cross Speedway flag on his handlebars, and a bird on the pillion."

"That wasn't a bird. That was my wife," Dave retorted.

"All I can say is you've got lots of wives. I've seen you," laughed Eddie.

"From the top of a 'bus, I bet," said Dave. "That's the riding you're best at . . . Bye-bye. For the duration . . ."

He pushed his machine over the tufted dunes, and on reaching the level sands, straddled it and opened out the engine. He wasn't satisfied till he was careering along the beach at nearly fifty miles an hour. With the throb of the engine and the crackle of the exhaust making sweet music in his ears, Dave felt life had become worth living again.

"Whoopee! . . ." he yelled at the top of his voice as, at the end of half a mile, he turned sharply with a broadside skid in professional dirt-track style that sent the sand up in a shower. By the time he had executed a couple of turns he had gathered quite a respectable crowd of spectators from the bored occupants of the beach, who were only too ready to welcome any diversion that promised relief from the monotony of existence in sand holes with nothing to do but sleep. When Dave alighted he was surrounded by a gratified little audience that included some of the gunners and a bombardier from his own regiment. He drew much self-satisfaction from the

interest he found himself the centre of.   In the middle
of describing, with no excess of modesty, the clever-
ness he had exhibited in salvaging his Norton, he was
interrupted by the appearance of his rival.   Eddie
had given his machine another overhaul, but the
engine was still not firing very well.   It continued to
function in a series of spasmodic bursts.

" Well, well . . .   If it isn't Eddie Harding with a
motor-cycle," jeered Dave to the special delight of
the men of his own regiment, who all knew the rivalry
that existed between the pair.   " Now I wonder what
he wants with a thing like that . . .   Eddie, you're
just in time.   The boys are all set for a race."

" Can't be done.   Not with an old crock like mine,"
grunted Eddie.   He knew he had small chance against
Dave's machine, and did not fancy being used as the
means of an easy triumph for his rival.

" Old crock ? " exclaimed Dave.   " It's a Norton,
isn't it, like mine ?   Same make, same model.   There's
only one slight difference, I can see."

" What's that ? "

" The rider."

The laugh that went up from the little crowd was
as much directed at the flagrant conceit of the
speaker as against his rival.   Eddie grinned good-
temperedly.

" I overlooked that," he said.   " With that handi-
cap, maybe your machine isn't any better than mine,
after all."

" Well, let's have a race, then," Dave urged.   " You
aren't afraid I shall beat you, are you ?   Only just
now you were boasting how you could nurse a bike.
That patient who sounds as if it's on its death-bed
gives you a chance of showing what you can do.   A
smart rider like you, Eddie, ought to be able to win
on anything."

" All right. I'll take you on," Eddie consented, after consideration.

A hearty cheer from the little cluster of troops greeted this announcement. A dirt-track race on Dunkirk beach was beyond their most sanguine expectations in the way of diversion. The gunners belonging to the Don R.'s regiment took the matter in hand as being their show. Under the direction of the bombardier they marked out on the sand a flattish oval course with a circumference of about half a mile. Markers were stationed to indicate the turns. The finishing post was the tail of a wrecked Heinkel on the rudder of which the bombardier, who appointed himself starter, hoisted his shirt. Dave and Eddie tossed for position, and Eddie won the inside berth. When they were lined up for the start, straddled over their machines, the bombardier stepped forward.

" Next event on the card," he shouted pompously. " Despatch Rider Dave Williams versus Despatch Rider Eddie Harding. . . . Four laps to the distance. . . . Any rider cutting the turns to be disqualified. . . . When I drop my right arm, that's the signal for the ' off ' . . . any questions, gentlemen ? . . . Then . . . get . . . ready. . . ."

He held up his right arm, paused for a second or two, and was just about to drop it when the anti-aircraft guns among the dunes suddenly roared out. In the distance, flying towards them appeared a formation of thirty German bombers with the puffs from the bursting ack-ack shells decorating their wake. Ten minutes earlier a patrol of Spitfires had flown over, but now the Germans had the sky to themselves.

The bombardier dropped his arm all right. And it served as the signal for a race in which everyone, spectators as well as riders, took part. A wild dash ensued for cover in the dunes. By the time the first bombs dropped the beach was deserted. Eddie and Dave were the last to vanish from view. In the first moment of excitement they darted off, leaving their machines behind. But after running twenty yards, as if on a common impulse, both returned, retrieved their treasures and shoved them as swiftly as they could towards safety. They crouched together in a deep dip in the dunes while the air shook with the thunder of exploding shells and bursting bombs.

When things quietened down they pushed their machines back to the beach again. The scattered spectators dribbled along from their holes to the starting post in twos and threes. The bombardier's shirt still hung from the Heinkel's rudder. More important was the fact that although some bombs had dropped very near, not one had fallen on the actual course. After giving the dispersed crowd time to collect again, the bombardier stepped forward with the intention of indulging himself for a second time in the preamble.

"Cut it out!" exclaimed Dave impatiently. "We've heard it all. Let's get on with the race before the Jerries drop another packet. Up with your arm, bombardier. We want to be off. If you're not quick, Eddie'll get cold feet."

The bombardier sent them away to a good start. Eddie's machine behaved, to begin with, better than he had expected. At the first turn he was well on Dave's tail, but down the second part of the straight Dave was able to draw clear and come over to the inner position. He rode in showy style, lying flat, with his body as near the petrol tank as possible. Eddie sat more upright. On approaching the second bend Dave glanced over his shoulder and grinned at Eddie. He was in the lead enough to negotiate the bend at an acute angle with a broadside skid. As the back wheel dragged, up went showers of sand to the great delight of the spectators. Eddie following behind, was half-blinded. He had to shut his eyes to keep out the grit. He swerved to get clear of the cloud Dave had put up, and lost further ground. After that there wasn't much else worth calling a race. Dave continued to draw away and finished a hundred and fifty yards ahead of his rival.

" Late again," he said, with a grin, as Eddie pulled up. " Only thing you won't be late for is getting back home."

" Not if I can help it," agreed Eddie. " It'll take a smarter fellow than Dave Williams to show me the way home to England when the time comes. That's a race you won't win, chum. I'll be off before the starter's let go the flag. I've had all I want of this bit of seaside."

" Quite right, Eddie," said Dave. " You'll be more comfortable on a boat than a bike."

" Hand over your bike," Eddie continued. " We'll have another race. Just to show the boys it was the machine, not the man that won."

Dave readily accepted the challenge. They exchanged machines and the bombardier sent them off again. Eddie, leading all the way, rode a sound, business-like race without any of the flashy stunts Dave had previously indulged in. The bombardier pronounced Eddie Harding the winner by a hundred yards.

" A hundred yards ! " exclaimed Dave. " That's as good as another win for me, Eddie. I got fifty more than you did out of your crock. And you didn't see me doing any nursing, either."

" Couldn't," Eddie corrected. " I was in front all the time."

" And I'll tell you what you couldn't find out for

yourself," continued Dave. " The trouble with your bike is . . ."

" A broken valve spring," interrupted Eddie, with a grin. " It's bouncing about all over the place. I discovered that on the first round."

" Now, boys. What about the decider ? " suggested the bombardier. " Can't let it rest at one all. It isn't a football game."

" I'm ready, if Eddie is," said Dave. " Each rides his own bike this time."

" I'll have to scrounge a new valve spring first," Eddie replied. " It's a wonder that machine of mine goes at all. Probably won't now Dave's done his worst to it."

" How long will you be ? " asked the bombardier.

" I ought to be able to lay hands on one in an hour."

" That's good enough," said Dave. He turned towards the little crowd of spectators. " Bye-bye for the present, boys," he cried exuberantly. " Roll up on the stroke of three and see the Dunkirk Speedway Derby won by Despatch Rider Dave Williams. . . . Admission free, and no collection. . . . Don't you be late, Eddie, or I shall claim the race," he shouted after his rival, who was already making his way towards the graveyard at the back of the dunes to begin his search for a new valve spring.

As three o'clock drew near quite a respectable crowd gathered on the beach to see the fun. The word had gone round, and lots of bored men were tempted from their holes in the sand. Twenty minutes before the race was timed to start the town, the dunes and the beaches were subjected to a very violent bombing attack. This fact favoured the size of the " gate." It was anticipated that there would be little likelihood of danger for another hour at least. The Germans kept pretty regular to their schedule.

It was now a fine afternoon. The sun had dissipated the haze and the sea, still calm as a mill-pond, glistened like burnished silver. The smoke-pall from burning Dunkirk, fed especially by the billowing fumes from the blazing oil tanks, hung steady in the windless air like a sombre ceiling through which the sunlight pierced in broad shafts. It was so hot that several of the spectators appeared in their sun-bathing garb.

" Makes me think I can hear the turnstiles clicking," Dave observed to the bombardier as he surveyed the cluster round the starting post. It flattered his vanity to be a performer in public.

" Wonder what's happened to Eddie," said the bombardier.

Dave had been wondering that, too. He hadn't expected Eddie would be absent more than half an hour. There must have been plenty of abandoned Nortons in the dunes where he could find the spare he needed.

Three o'clock came and no sign of Eddie.

" What are you going to do about it ? " asked the bombardier.

" Oh, give him another quarter of an hour," said Dave. " That fellow's always late. I'll be generous. Mustn't disappoint the boys, either."

What Dave really meant was that he did not want to disappoint himself. He wanted his show, and began to feel a bit uneasy lest he should be deprived of it.

Another quarter of an hour passed without Eddie putting in an appearance. Dave displayed distinct signs of annoyance.

" You win, Dave," said the bombardier, looking at his watch.

" To hell with that," replied Dave. " I want a

race. Not a gift. . . . Give him till half-past. He'll turn up."

But he felt less confident now than he sounded. An explanation was formulating itself in his mind to account for Eddie's absence. And it was an explanation he did not relish at all. Nevertheless, as the minutes passed, the conviction strengthened that he was right.

As it neared half-past three, and the prospects of another visit soon from the German bombers increased, the little crowd of spectators decided that the race was a wash-out and dwindled away to their cover in the dunes. Soon only a few gunners from Dave's regiment and the bombardier remained.

" Time's up," announced the bombardier, at last.

" Wait a bit. . . . I'll just give him my theme song," said Dave. " If he's anywhere near, he'll answer."

He sounded on his horn a distinctive variety of long and short blasts. No response came from the direction of the dunes.

" Race awarded to Despatch Rider Dave Williams. . . . By default," declared the bombardier pompously, and without any further ceremony. He was tired of waiting and wanted to retire to his hole in the sand before the next attack.

" I'd never have believed it of Eddie ! " exclaimed Dave in disgust, letting his machine fall flat on the sand.

" Believe what ? " inquired the bombardier.

" He's got a lift in a boat home," pursued Dave bitterly. " That's what's happened to him. Didn't he say he'd beat me there all right. Well, he's done what he said he would. I win the bike race by default, and he wins the boat-race. What a pal. . . . To walk out on you like that. . . ."

But Dave was mistaken. He was destined to be the winner of both races. And both by default. Even as he poured out his grievance to the bombardier, Eddie Harding had been relegated to the position of a non-starter in the boat race, too. He was lying face upwards in the dunes between Malo-les-Bains and Dunkirk, his Norton beside him. A bomb splinter had taken away the side of his head. In his hand he clutched a new valve spring.

A DUNKIRK DIARY

XI—A Dunkirk Diary

[*Being some unregretted hours in the life of Lieutenant Eric Martin, 555th Field Regiment, R.A.*]

JUNE 3RD. 7.30 A.M.—No danger of oversleeping, although I had a very late night. Alarum went off punctually. (Twenty German bombers assisted by a lot of ack-ack fire). Wished my sandhole in the dunes was a mile deep. Very wide-awake by the time it was over. Hope it's true that sleeping in clothes saturated with sea water does you good. Mine are still damp and sticky. Think I'll be more comfortable stripped, anyway.

Pleased to find I have woke up irritable. That means I am my normal self still, despite much recent and undesired encouragement to turn into something weird and strange.

Irritation gradually coheres round loss of my great-coat. Feel two ways about this. One, that it's absurd to get annoyed at a time like this over such a trifle. Two, that it's a healthy sign. Perhaps it isn't such " a time like this," after all, or I shouldn't be worrying.

But I must say, I feel sore with Hart-Davis. I'd set my heart on getting that greatcoat home. Last night, when we started off for the beaches he asked me to lend it to him. He had a bit of a cold and thought it would keep him nice and warm while he was standing in the sea waiting for a boat. I agreed on one condition. In return for the comfort he obtained from my coat, Hart-Davis was to love and cherish it till we both reached England. And if he got there first, he was to take care of it till he was able to return it to me. This he swore solemnly to do.

The upshot of it was, he managed to get on a boat, I didn't, and I got a message from him that at the last moment he had handed my greatcoat to So-and-so. Of course, So-and-so had handed it to So-and-so, and that was the end of it. I hope his damn cold develops into a stinker. . . .

* * * * *

8 A.M.—Breakfast. Ration biscuit washed down with a mouthful of gin. (Drinking water unobtainable. Haven't had a drop for nearly two days.) Feel a different man and a half. Always the same with me after a hearty breakfast.

A score or so of other fellows are dug in the dunes within a hundred yards of me. Some of them gunners from the battery. " Nice morning . . ." we inform one another. So it is, if sand and sunshine's all you want.

Hailed by Jimmie Good, our Battery Commander, now like me, in a state of extreme mufti. He dwells in the next hole but one. Jimmie is a pleasant-looking fellow, and an old friend of mine. But I think it will be some time before his face ceases to remind me of a few minutes I never wish to live over again, not even in memory. Jimmie got me badly rattled last night. He may not know it. But I do.

Yesterday afternoon I was sent from the Battery to report at R.H.Q. which was in a brickfield a mile behind our positions outside Dunkirk. When I arrived George Anderson, from the other battery of the regiment, was already there.

" I want you to reconnoitre the approaches to the beach for your batteries when they come out of action to-night," the Colonel said to us. " Then you can guide them in the dark."

George and I started off at once in my truck. We crossed the canal by the bridge near Rosendaal, drove to Malo-les-Bains, and footed it over the dunes to the promenade in the direction of Dunkirk. After proceeding some distance we ran up against a line of French infantry with fixed bayonets, drawn across the promenade. They halted us a bit too peremptorily to be pleasant. A very snappy sous-officier informed us that we were not allowed to go any farther, as that part of the promenade and beach was reserved for French troops. Which seemed so unlikely that we didn't believe it. George and I looked at each other.

" I'd like to argue the point," he said savagely. " But there aren't enough of us."

" My views coincide," I said.

So we worked back to the truck and then drove along a road parallel to the promenade behind the burning houses. After a while we turned down another road at right-angles which brought us out close to the Mole. The shelling was enough to keep one from loitering, so taking a look at our bearings I decided it would be a good route for the Battery that night.

At eleven o'clock the Battery blew up its guns and started for the beach. About fifty men, all told, in five 15-cwt trucks. Being guide, I rode in the first with Jimmie Good seated next to me. The Colonel's orders were to abandon the vehicles the other side of Rosendaal and march from there to the beach. We

passed through the village, pulled-up, and were about
to destroy the vehicles when I suggested to Jimmie :

" Let's save ourselves a bit of foot-slogging. I
don't see why we shouldn't take the trucks as near
to the Mole as possible. This afternoon I went down
a road that came out within four hundred yards of it."

" Good idea," said Jimmie. " Sure you know the
way ? "

" Blindfolded," I replied confidently. I took the
driving-wheel of the first truck and we rumbled
forward again.

" I'll admit that before Jimmie began giving me
the jumps, I was beginning to wonder a bit myself.
Places don't look the same in the night as they do by
day. Besides, every now and then the darkness was
lit up with the flash from a bursting shell, and in that
sort of light nothing looked recognisable. Another
thing, it did seem to me that we were longer than I
expected in reaching the road leading to the Mole.
But I was still confident I hadn't made a mistake.

Then Jimmie grew restive. " Are you sure you're
going the right way ? " he demanded.

" I think so," I replied.

" Think . . . ! " he cried. " Damn it ! . . . You've
got to be certain."

" Well, I am," I said. And from that moment I
wasn't.

Every yard we progressed I could sense Jimmie
becoming more and more uneasy. It reacted on me.
Soon I, too, was wallowing in a stew of uncertainty.
We went on, the shells swishing overhead and crashing into buildings. Down they tumbled on either
side of us with a thunder of falling metal and masonry,
and the tearing of wood. It was a hell of a jolt for
the nerves, in any circumstances. What made it
worse for me was that I began asking myself : " Am

I going to be responsible for leading these men to their doom ? " The answer I got was a profuse sweat.

" Aren't we ever coming to this bloody road ? " said Jimmie, giving me no peace. " Are you sure you're not taking us into a mess ? "

I didn't answer. I wasn't sure of anything. My confidence had been torn to shreds. And when Jimmie added fiercely : " I wish to God I'd never listened to you, and had destroyed the vehicles," even the shreds went.

At last Jimmie refused to proceed a yard more without some encouragement. So we halted and took a compass bearing. It showed that, at least, we weren't going backwards. Then a shell burst not far away, and in the flash I saw something that kicked a hundred-ton weight off my mind.

" Here's the road. . . . A little farther, on the right," I said, as though I'd never had any doubt about it. At the same time I felt savage with Jimmie for making me sweat so unnecessarily.

But another sweat awaited me. The road leading to the Mole was a very different road from the one I had traversed in the afternoon. Fifty yards down on the left-hand side, a large shop was blazing furiously. There was another bonfire a little farther along, on the opposite side. When the breeze blew the flames leaped across the road. At times the place looked like a lane of fire. Several of the other buildings had been hit by shells, and lumps of masonry were crashing into the street without warning.

" This is a bloody fine mess you've dragged us into," said Jimmie, reviling me bitterly. " I'm damned if I go a step more in the vehicles."

We alighted and put the trucks out of action. Then, in twos and threes, our party made crouching dashes down the centre of the street whenever the flames retreated a bit.   There were one or two narrow shaves, but we all got through safely, and continued down the slope to the beach.

As the Mole was being shelled heavily with shrapnel we tacked ourselves on to what looked to be the shortest queue.   It wasn't short enough for us, however.   After standing several hours in the sea without getting our turn for a boat, dawn broke.   Evacuation for that night was over.   Daylight would bring the bombers.   So we retired to the shelter of the dunes to hope for the best, and wait till night gave us another chance of getting off.

*　　　*　　　*　　　*　　　*

10 A.M.—Heinkels over again.   Third visit since daylight.   They plaster the town, the dunes and the beaches.   No attempt to dive-bomb.   They fly low on an even keel, dropping their stuff with impunity. Occasionally someone on the beach takes a pot at them with a rifle.   Not far from me a fellow lets go with a revolver.   Futile, of course.   But the feeling is you must have a shot at them, even if only with half a brick.   It's as exasperating as that.   They sweep up and down the beach, drenching it with machine-gun fire.   A long, swishy roar.   The bullets whip up the sand into a curved, travelling wave, like surf breaking on a beach.

I decide that my home is a little too humble in the circumstances.   Roof it in with a bonnet I've wrenched off a dismantled Vauxhall car.   Cover this with as much sand as I can heap up.   Some empty metal two-pounder shell-boxes come in handy for the walls. Bank these with plenty of sand.   Result, a kennel at which the meanest mongrel would turn up its nose. But I'm not proud any longer.   It may look crude, but it gives me a sense of security. Mistaken, no doubt. Still . . .

I lie crouched inside with my head out of the opening, seeing life.

*   *   *   *   *

10.30 A.M.—" Sand Castles " is evidently the game here. But I never was good at it, even as a kid. So I content myself with being a critic. Within a stone's throw of my kennel half a dozen separate artists are busy on designs, some modest, some pretentious. The nearest fellow to me has produced something elaborate. I say it is a praiseworthy representation of the nuptial confectionery you see in Buszard's shop window. He says it's St. Paul's Cathedral.

It's more than a bit incongruous to see grown-up men in battle-dress, with shells plopping round them, engrossed in a pastime one only associates with happy kids on a peaceful seaside beach. Makes one realise what a queer twist has come over things.

" Sand Castles " in the dunes strikes me as being hard work. The sand is so fine and dry that the vibration from quite distant shell-bursts starts it running away in little rills. The builder has to be constantly effecting repairs or his edifice dissolves into a shapeless mass before his eyes. No denying, though, it's a most useful occupation for the purpose of killing a stretch of really lousy time.

*   *   *   *   *

11 A.M.—A coming event has cast its shadow before. The shadow (substantial) is the Colonel's servant, Pilcher. That means the Colonel himself is in the offing. I'd been wondering what had happened to him. If he'd crossed during the night I was sure

he'd feel annoyed when he discovered some of the regiment had been left behind. The C.O.'s ideas on this subject are short and simple. Like the captain of a sinking ship, he believes it his sacred duty to be the last to go.

Hail Pilcher, who is wandering about the dunes as if searching for something. He informs me that the C.O. has not long arrived on the beach from R.H.Q. with him are the Adjutant and the Battery Quarter-Master-Sergeant. They have a fairish hole in the sand at the top of the beach about a quarter of a mile away. The Colonel, says Pilcher, is anxious to collect all information possible as to who got away, who didn't, and where the bits are now. I say I'll run over and tell him all I know as soon as I throw some clothes on.

" By the way, sir," says Pilcher, " you don't happen to have seen a vacant deck-chair anywhere, I suppose ? "

" No, you old scrounger," I laugh. " Try East-bourne."

Jimmie Good, who has developed into an excellent local newspaper, gives me the latest rumour on the beach. Only 5,000 out of the expected 25,000 British troops got off last night, says the story, owing to the fact that the French rushed the British portion of the beaches and completely upset the organisation. Being one of the 20,000 who, if the story is true, ought to be in England by now instead of sweltering on this stinking beach, a target for high-velocity shells and dive-bombers, I curse, appropriately, the authors of my undoing.

*   *   *   *   *

11.30 A.M.—Report to the Colonel and tell him all I know about who's here and who's there. He is

seated in a deck-chair. Another triumph for Pilcher.
I believe that fellow could get the Colonel anything.

"Keep in touch," says the C.O. "I'm hoping for
some official information this afternoon about to-night's
arrangements."

Able to assure him heartily that he would find me
waiting on the doorstep.

On my way back, after dodging a couple of shells,
stop for a few minutes' chat with an infantry major
and a brace of subalterns who are tinkering very
earnestly with the inside of a pale-blue speed-boat,
drawn up at the end of the promenade. They tell me
they have been on the job since dawn, and are going
to make that engine work, or bust in the attempt.
In the former event they intend making a dash to
England. I wish them " all the best."

*   *   *   *   *

12.30 P.M.—Bombers again. They've missed the
Spitfire patrol. Or the other way round. They don't
do much damage in my district, beyond shaking down
a few sand castles. Of course, they can't resist having
a go at the wrecked tanker which is lying a few hundred
yards off the beach. Comic, the fascination this poor
old barge has for the Boche airmen. It was bombed
days ago, and has been lying off the shore a deserted
wreck ever since. Yet every time the bombers come
over they make it a target. And usually they miss
badly. Have they a spite against it because it persists
in not sinking ? It has become quite a joke on the
beach. We emerge from our holes (slightly) to watch
the fun.

Jimmie Good takes me along to see another
phenomenon of the beach. Fifty yards away, in a
very narrow but deep hole scooped in the sand, a
couple of signallers are sound asleep. There is so

little room that they are almost locked in each other's arms. I am informed that they fell asleep at dawn, and have shown not the slightest sign of waking since, despite four heavy bombing attacks, and heaven knows how much shell fire. The sand has trickled down the sides of their hole, half covering them. The Babes in the Dunes. . . . They are the envy of everybody. Think what they are missing. . . .

*   *   *   *   *

1 P.M.—Lunch. Ration biscuit, washed down with mouthful of gin. Very hot. The heat, reflected off the dunes, hits you like the blast from a furnace. Sun-bathing is now a rival to sand-castles, which is too strenuous.

There's a drawback to sun-bathing here. It's a dirty job. Your body gets covered with smuts from the burning oil tanks. The atmosphere is thick with them. They are oily smuts, so when you try to brush them off your skin they leave black smears. When you can't stand the sight of yourself any longer you go for a swim. And come back looking worse. The sea is covered with a scum of smuts from the same source.

Shelling grows more intense. Dunkirk gets it badly, and more buildings on the promenade begin to blaze. Four or five massive plumes of smoke rise in the air, as if volcanoes are in eruption. They flatten out over the town and beach in a sort of dingy grey ceiling, behind which the sun looks a bit pale.

My indefatigable newspaper (Jimmie) informs me that the Germans have mounted a battery of heavy guns on the beach in front of Nieuport, and are pounding us from there. Later on, when the shelling dies down to normal, I learn from the same newspaper that it is because a French coastal battery the other side of the Mole, took them on with good results.

Some casualties among the troops scattered over the beach. Parties of the R.A.M.C. go round. They bury the dead on the spot, and cart the wounded off to hospital, where, by the way, they are doomed to remain till the Germans arrive, as it has been found impossible to evacuate any more wounded, except walking cases. A padre goes round with these parties. It is owing to their constant attention, especially after the bombers have had a session, that the beach now remains comparatively free from the spectacle of dead and wounded lying about.

The worst horror on the beach is a dead horse. There's nothing like a dead horse for stinking the place out, especially in this heat. You can smell him everywhere. If one of the R.A.M.C. parties would only bury him we'd all recommend them for the V.C.

*   *   *   *   *

2 P.M.—Another heavy attack. The Babes in the Dunes still asleep, lucky devils. Jimmie says he feels towards them as he used to feel towards the fellow who won the Irish Sweep. . . . Even if they wake now, they've managed to blot out half of this dreary, monotonous, futile sort of day. This day is like a hyphen between a couple of names ; it means nothing in itself. Everyone wants to see it over and done with. A meaningless link between something that went before and something that's to come. If ever time deserved to be killed, this day does. . . .

Jimmie and I decide to go for a swim. Half a mile out, to the left of the wrecked tanker, is a small cargo sailing-boat that shows no signs of life, though she appears intact. We swim out to investigate. For some unknown reason the vessel has been abandoned.

We prowl round and find that the owners have left behind in the cabin a dozen loaves of English white bread. Our eyes pop out of our heads. It's the first bread we have seen for ten days. What a find ! . . .

Straightaway we sit down in the cabin and gnaw a loaf into nothing, then load the rest into the dinghy, pull ashore, and convey it as secretly as possible up to the dunes. While I keep guard over it in my kennel, Jimmie darts round the dunes from hole to hole telling all our gunners he can round-up to hurry along to my kennel for some rations. When they collect, I count the ravenous mouths and cut each man a slice with my jack-knife. The last half loaf I keep for the Colonel's party.

The C.O. appreciates it as much as the men. He, also, hasn't eaten bread for ten days. But the Adjutant enjoys it most. It gives him a chance of indulging once more in his speciality—bully-beef sandwich *à la* strawberry jam. He arranges a slab of bully-beef on a slice of bread, plasters the top of it with jam an inch thick, and clamps down the mess with another lump of bread.

" Glorious ! " . . . he exclaims as his teeth dig into it. " You are a fool not to try it."

" I've turned vegetarian," I say. I may be craving for a change of diet, but I'm not so far gone as to be able to face up to strawberry jam on bully-beef. No one else has the courage to try, either.

" I'd like to know how you come to be in possession of jam," I ask.

" Simple," he replies. " Pilcher. He rescued it from a wrecked ration lorry. Also a tin of condensed milk, if you'd like to try that."

" No, thanks," I say. " I'm thirsty enough."

*   *   *   *   *

3.15 P.M.—Bombers, of course. But the Colonel has received information that livens things up for us much more. A determined effort is to be made by the Navy to-night to evacuate the entire remaining British troops.

Grand news, this. Lots of us have already been speculating on the unlovely prospect of another day in sand-holes. A sudden dread overtakes me. Suppose I am one of the two who are sure to get left behind. . . .

It's only a flash through the mind, but it gives me the creeps. Must make sure I'm not late for this appointment with the Navy.

The C.O. starts off with the Adjutant on a tour of inspection of the beach and town to round up all the parties from the regiment he can find and tell them not to fail to make their way to the Mole by half-past nine. He is most anxious that not a man shall be forgotten.

*　　　*　　　*　　　*　　　*

4 P.M.—The Battery Quartermaster-Sergeant strolls up to my kennel.

" I've found some tea, sir," he says sadly. " If only I'd a Primus stove."

" Have a look the other side of that dune," I reply casually.

When he does so and finds there really is a Primus there, he is ready to accord me full honours as a magician. He thought he was asking for the moon. Actually, when he mentioned a Primus I did recall having seen one earlier in the day at that spot. But I didn't spoil the effect on the B.Q.M.S. by explaining. It must have impressed him with a belief in my supernatural powers. From now hence, at intervals, he continually wanders over, inviting me to perform other miracles.

" Could I oblige him with the loan of a fountain pen with some ink in it ? . . ."

" Had I change for a pound note, so that he'd have some small silver when he landed in England ? . . ."

I was content to have produced some supernatural tea. And never did tea taste like something better than this world. The Primus had enough juice in it to boil up a dixie, and we imbibed it from mess-tins, having sweetened it with some of the Adjutant's condensed milk. I found it so soothing that for the first time that day I was able afterwards to recline in my kennel and emulate the Babes in the Dunes. For an hour only. Then the bombers came, curse 'em, and spoilt it.

*   *   *   *   *

6.30 P.M.—There's no place like home. . . . Be it ever so humble. . . . I know it all now.

If anyone had told me a couple of hours ago that my kennel in the dunes could have inspired such feelings in me, I'd have dismissed him as the craziest of the crazy, and no pal of mine, either. And I'd have been wrong.

After the bombers had thoroughly spoilt my nap, and left me very bad tempered, I thought I'd kill some more of this ugly time by another swim out to the sailing-boat. I went alone. Jimmie was asleep. It would have been brutal to wake him. I climbed aboard and was making another exploration of the cabins, when I heard the sound of a motor engine close by. Going up on deck what should I see but the pale-blue speed-boat which the infantry trio had been tinkering with on the promenade in the morning. Evidently they had succeeded in their repairs. They drew up alongside and a subaltern in the stern hailed me.

" Hello, Sinbad.   Any charts aboard ? "

" Only an old one of the Thames Estuary," I replied, having noticed it already in the chart locker.

" Chuck it down, will you ?   It might come in useful."

When I reappeared on deck again the subaltern penetrated my disguise.

" You're the gunner bloke, aren't you ? " he said. " Didn't recognise you at first in your birthdays. What about a trip in the old *Skylark* ?   Room for another one.   Nice afternoon trip round the North Foreland.   No return fares."

I remembered then they had told me they were going to make a dash for England.   There were four of them now.   They had picked up another major and he sat up in front next to the pilot.

The sudden invitation gave me a jump.   I looked back and saw the dirty smudge on the coast that was Dunkirk.   I looked the other way and saw (or imagined I did) England.   It was a bit of a risk, of course.   On the other hand, it would mean several hours less for me on that sickening beach.   And by this time, like everyone else, I was bored stiff with it.   Anything to get away.

I couldn't make up my mind at first what was holding me back.   Then I knew.   I was stark naked. The idea of landing on my native heath without even woad, required a little digesting.   If I'd had my battle dress on, or even the right half of it, I'd have been in that speed-boat like a shot.   As it was, I hesitated.   I came very near refusing the offer when I had an inspiration.

" Half a minute," I shouted.

I dashed down to the cabin and in no time was

back again with a reefer jacket buttoned round my waist like a kilt. The subaltern grinned.

"Hurry up, miss," he cried. "Don't keep the party waiting."

I lowered myself over the side of the vessel and dropped into the boat. The two fellows in the stern made room for me between them, "in case I felt cold," and off we started for England.

Nobody gave a thought to the possibility that we might not get there. We were all too happy putting the miles between ourselves and Dunkirk. On the contrary, we made estimates of the hour of our arrival. After making due allowance for the fact that none of us had any experience in handling motor-boats, that the engine was working groggily, that we had no charts, that there was some uncertainty about the sufficiency of our petrol, we came to general agreement that we could consider ourselves damned unlucky if we didn't reach the Promised Land shortly after nightfall. Such optimism could only have been bred from the peculiar brand of pessimism engendered by a spell of monotonous hours on Dunkirk dunes.

We chugged along quite merrily for nearly an hour, but not at speed-boat speed. The engine saw to that. Still, we had nothing to grumble at. The sun shone brilliantly from a sky that, now we had got beyond the Dunkirk smoke-pall, was magnificently blue and clear. A nice warm breeze had sprung up, strong enough to make the water alive and interesting. Some distance in front we could see small black humps appearing for a moment or two above the surface and then disappearing. I counted about six of them bobbing up in different places, now and again.

"Amusing little devils, porpoises," said the subaltern on my right. "Ever watched a school ? "

" This school looks more like an isolation hospital,"
I said.

They were, in fact, rather scattered, each making
a solo turn of its little gambol.

We drew nearer, on a course that would take us
through the middle of them. Suddenly there was a
terrific yell in my ear. The subaltern on my right
had jumped to his feet, and with horror in his eyes
was yelling :

" Stop her ! . . . Stop the boat ! . . ."

I thought he had suddenly gone mad. The pilot
glanced over his shoulder. I could see he thought the
same.

" Stop the boat . . ." the subaltern continued to
yell frantically. " We're in a minefield. . . . We've
just missed hitting one. . . . It nearly nudged us.
. . . I saw it. . . ."

Next second we all saw it—or another like it. About
twenty feet away, on our left front, an evil-looking
black hump equipped with nasty horns bobbed up
for a moment above the surface of the water. Then
a wave washed over it, and it disappeared from view.
But one look at it was enough.

And we had fondly imagined they were porpoises. . . .

I don't know what sort of mines they were, whether
British or German. That they were mines was
sufficient for all of us. The hush that descended on
that boat would have done credit to a death-bed.
The pilot had cut off the engine instantly, and now we
were just drifting while we recovered from the shock.
No one uttered a word. I expected any moment to
be blown sky-high. I suppose the others did, too,
judging from the expressions on their faces. I didn't
think it possible to have felt so scared. I knew
what it was to be dive-bombed. And I knew all
about heavy shell-fire. But, believe me, that's a

picnic compared with sitting out there on the wide, wide sea in a little boat in the middle of a minefield, just waiting. . . . There was something about those sinister hidden devils, bobbing up now and again to give you a wicked leer as much as to say: " You won't even know when——" that froze one up.

The Major who was piloting the boat pulled himself together.

" Anybody feel like going on ? " he asked tersely.

Four heads shook vigorously. God knows, we all loathed the sight of Dunkirk beach. But at that moment all we wanted was to be safely back on it.

Very gingerly we put the boat under weigh again, and turned her nose in the direction whence we had come. We travelled at a crawl, hoping that if we did bump against anything the impact would be gentle enough not to start a bang. That, of course, prolonged the agony. Whenever a mine bobbed up in the vicinity we shuddered lest another might do the same right underneath us. I found myself staring all the time with fixed eyes at the planks in the bottom of the boat.

When at last it was all over and done with, and we ran the boat safely on the beach, we just walked away and left it, exchanging hardly a word. If I'd owned a mirror I'm certain I should have looked to see if I'd gathered any grey hair. . . .

On my way to the kennel I passed the Babes in the Dunes. They were still blissfully sleeping. . . . What luck some fellows have ! . . .

*   *   *   *   *

7.30 P.M.—Bombers have come and gone. It is expected to be their last trip for the day. They make it memorable for us. The attack is a heavy one and lasts for over a quarter of an hour. Dunkirk, the

dunes and the beaches all get it hot. Only consolation
is that a couple of them seem to have been badly
winged by ack-ack fire, and probably won't get home.

A strange apparition appears on the dunes from the
North. It is mounted on a black horse, and wears a
general's cap with red band, a blue silk pyjama coat,
a pair of riding breeches, and some highly-polished
boots, of a deep mahogany hue, that glisten in the
evening sun.

It is some facetious Tommy who has dressed himself up. He rides up and down the beach, stopping
every now and then to stand up in the stirrups, with
his hand shading his eyes in Wild West style, asking
with tremendous seriousness : " Anybody seen any
Indians pass this way ? "

As a piece of absurdity it goes down well, following
the bombers. To me it seems a fitting close to a day
that has simply reeked of unreality from beginning
to end. A crazy mixture of tragedy, farce, boredom,
thirst and futility.

Much self-control needed not to start for the Mole
straightaway. But there's no sense in getting there
before nightfall. The ships won't pull in till dark.
And the Germans are sure to concentrate their shells
on it. Safer to stay here. But these last two waiting
hours are going to prove trying.

*   *   *   *   *

On board H.M. Destroyer :—England next stop !
. . . I can scarcely believe it is all over. But Jimmie
assures me it isn't a dream. We really have been
evacuated. . . .

At half-past nine Jimmie and I set out for the Mole.
Passed the Babes in the Dunes standing outside their
hole, shaking themselves free from sand. They'd
obliterated the whole day, and timed their wake-up

for exactly the right moment.   What an instinct. . . .
I don't suppose they'll ever realise how much they
have to be thankful for.

It was fairly dark.   We proceeded along the
promenade, and about four hundred yards from the
Mole began to encounter dead bodies, the latest
victims of the enemy shell fire.   This had now become
intense.   The shrapnel was continually bursting overhead.   Every now and then a figure dropped to the
ground in the darkness.   The bodies of those killed
earlier on had been covered with blankets.   The new
casualties remained as they fell.   There was no more
time for niceties.   On the Mole itself bloodstained
bandages were strewn all over the place.   They may
have been cast off at the last moment by men who
feared that if they were seen to be wounded they
would not be evacuated, although this rule only
applied to bad cases.

The Colonel arrived with the Adjutant and the rest
of his party.   We gradually made our way on to the
Mole, along which the very last remnants of the
B.E.F. were streaming in their thousands.   Little
groups of gunners from our own regiment emerged
out of the darkness and tacked themselves on to us
as we slowly moved up in the crowd.   The petrol
tanks on the other side of the Mole still flared away,
sending up great hissing tongues of flame two hundred
feet into the air.   A terrifying torch to lighten us on
our way.   Colossal billows of smoke blew over us.

At last we reached the end of the Mole.   Our turn
had come at last.   We waited hours, or so it seemed
to me, with the shrapnel cracking overhead and the
dread in one's heart that it was still not too late to
miss the bus.

Suddenly out of the dark sea crept, swiftly and
silently, a destroyer.   It pulled up alongside the Mole,

not tying up, so as to be ready for a quick get-away. Directly it was close enough the troops began to jump on to the deck.

The Colonel stood by, watching his party get on board. When he had seen the last man go, and not before, he himself jumped.

And then the Adjutant, who knew the C.O.'s firm resolve to be the last of the regiment to leave France, played a joke on him. He hopped off the destroyer on to the Mole, waited a second or two, and jumped back again.

The Colonel smiled.

" BATTLES LONG AGO "

XII—" BATTLES LONG AGO "

To them already it seemed long, long ago, though only the space of a few hours separated them from it. Time can play such tricks, fortunately for us, and transfer a painful yesterday into the dim and distant past with the speed of a departing comet.

Besides, those few hours had contained for them so much that was unexpected, as well as much that was different. This it was that so powerfully emphasised the separation. First, there had been that amazing welcome. A band to meet them. The entire population of the West Country town lining the streets from the railway to the barracks in the sweet English June sunshine. . . . The cheering, the waving, the smiling through tears. . . . Babies in their mothers' arms shaking little Union Jacks. More like the welcome home to a band of conquering heroes than to a fragment of a broken army. And the last thing in the world they had expected was to be greeted as heroes. . . . Weary as they were, they found it a bit bewildering.

Then, on their arrival at the depot of the County Regiment, had followed the Colonel's little speech of welcome that touched them so deeply. The Colonel, a tall, elderly man with iron-grey hair had been called from the Reserve on the outbreak of war to take charge of the depot. He faced the shabby, scarecrow band of officers who stood grouped in the sunshine outside the Mess, the bright light vividly revealing their worn faces and oddments of clothes, upon which white incrustations of salt were visible where the sea-water had dried. The Colonel's lip trembled. A picture rose before him of these men, patiently standing in the sea off Dunkirk beach waiting hour after hour till their turn came for rescue. The moisture glistened in his eyes. On his breast he sported a line and a half of decorations. And he was thinking as he stood there, that there wasn't a man in front of him who had not earned as much by his sufferings in the past three weeks.

" Officers of the British Expeditionary Force . . ." he began, a trifle unsteadily. " It gives me the greatest pleasure to welcome you to our depot. Believe me, when I say that in the whole of my career I have never received an honour I appreciate more signally than to have you as my guests. I feel . . . I feel . . ."

But he could not express in words what he felt, so after a pause he proceeded :

" I want you all to regard this place as your temporary home. I trust you will find it comfortable. Make yourselves free of it. I am proud to put the barracks at your disposal. . . . There will be a little discipline, naturally. But don't let that worry you. . . . And a little work, such as reclothing and reorganising the men in sections for food and recreation. Otherwise, I do not propose putting any restrictions on you at all. Beyond the fact that you must not go beyond the town without my permission."

He dropped into a confidential tone :

" One last word . . . from an old hand. . . . Pack in all the sleep you can. . . ."

Then he departed to address the N.C.O.s and men in similar strain.

A Captain who was President of the Regimental Institutes next took them in hand to show them their sleeping accommodation. Emergency bedrooms had been installed in the billiards-room. In the regular bedrooms four beds now occupied the place of one. Lecture rooms and covered miniature ranges had been reserved for the troops to sleep in.

Dragging sore and heavy feet behind them the little crowd of officers shuffled behind the P.R.I. into the barracks. He opened the door of a large room on the ground floor lit by three big windows looking out on to the lawn. It was bright and airy, but rather empty. Apart from five single iron beds, neatly made-up with their white pillows and brown army blankets the room contained no other furniture.

" We'll put Majors in here," said the P.R.I.

But there were only four Majors, so he picked on a Gunner Captain.

" You can make the fifth," he said.

The five men who were strangers and had never before exchanged a word, pushed into the room they were now to share in company, glancing more attentively at one another than at their new surroundings. They were all in battle dress of various stages of decay except the young Gunner Captain who disported tunic, breeches and puttees, much smeared with oil, and with a long rent in one knee of the breeches. Although the day was very warm he still wore the heavy greatcoat in which he had stood for hours in the sea at Dunkirk awaiting his turn to be evacuated. The sun had dried it into stiff folds with edges hard as boards. Two of the Majors were infantry men from different regiments, and presented a curious contrast. Both were tall and about thirty-five

years of age. But one was as fair as the other
was dark. The dark Major possessed a thin, long,
gloomy face. He was of the disposition known as
reserved, and one glance sufficed to show that a casual
word from him would be something in the nature of
a miracle.

The fair-haired Major, blue-eyed and fresh com-
plexioned, threatened, on the other hand, to release a
torrent of words at any moment. Actually, not a
word passed his lips. But the effort by which he
enforced this silence was as patent as the presence of
the nervous impulses prompting him to ejaculation.
His movements were restless and jerky, and his eyes,
never devoid of a haunted expression, shot quick,
furtive glances everywhere.

The quartette of Majors was completed by a fat,
round-faced, jolly-looking man from an Anti-Tank
gun regiment, and a very tired R.A.M.C. doctor who
rounded off every remark he made with the same
high-pitched giggle.

" Nice room, this," remarked the Anti-Tank Major
to the P.R.I. as he surveyed the lofty white ceiling,
and the duck-egg blue painted walls of their new
quarters.

" Yes. One of the most cheerful in the barracks,"
replied the P.R.I. " It's the Card Room. The
regiment have always been terrible bridge addicts.
Got quite a name for it. . . ." Then, feeling a trifle
self-conscious after this observation in the present
circumstances, he made a quick exit.

" Card Room . . . Bridge . . . That takes you back
a few centuries, doesn't it ? " exclaimed the Anti-Tank
Major, with a laugh, to his companions. He ruminated
a moment or two, and added : " Well, I'll bet all the
kit I left behind at Dunkirk that this room has never
in its life seen riskier bids than I've been seeing in

the last three weeks.   And the stakes weren't sixpence
a hundred either."

" That's what comes of joining a Suicide Club," the
Gunner Captain observed.

" Oh, I wouldn't call it that," replied the other
cheerfully.   " The Anti-Tanks provide you with the
spice of life—variety.   When you grow a bit bored with
being a gunner you can indulge in all the excitements of being an infantryman.   And what
excitements. . . ."

The fair-haired Major, who had been standing
stiffly with his back towards them, gazing out
of the window, suddenly swung round on his
heels.

" For God's sake, shut up ! . . ." he cried, in an
outburst of anger.   " Isn't there anything else in the
world for you to talk about ? . . ."

The four others stared at him, amazed.

" What world have you in mind ? " inquired the
Gunner Captain coldly.   He did not relish this form
of interruption.

The R.A.M.C. Major nudged him.

" Better say nothing," he muttered.   " The man
doesn't look too well."

So they all relapsed into silence, divesting themselves of their tin-hats, gasbags and their webbing.

The fair-haired Major returned to his occupation of
staring through the window.   After a minute or two
he rejoined his companions with a charming smile
which almost banished the haunted expression from
his eyes.

" I most humbly apologise for being so devilish
rude just now," he said, with a shy frankness.   " I'm
tired out . . .   A bit on edge, I think . . .   I'll be
all right after a brandy and soda.   I think I'll slip
out and see if I can get one . . ."   He smiled again.

"I see you all forgive me . . ." he said, and quitted the room.

*   *   *   *   *

And now it was night, and the five men were once more gathered together in the ex-Card Room preparing to turn-in. They sat on the edge of their iron bed-steads undressing in easy stages. An orderly had drawn the black-out blinds, and placed a small table in the centre of the room, furnishing it with a decanter of water and a half-dozen glasses. The fair-haired Major, the only one who had not begun to undress, poured out a tumblerful with a shaky hand, and swallowed it at a gulp. Then he sat on the edge of his bed again, staring at the brown linoleum on the floor, his fingers locked together in front of him, burning-up cigarette after cigarette.

"It seems ages since I went to bed," observed the R.A.M.C. Major, adding his meaningless, high-pitched giggle.

"I'd enjoy it more if I had a pair of pyjamas," the Anti-Tank Major remarked. "I suppose nobody possesses such a thing . . ."

"I'm sleeping in my pants," said the Gunner Captain.

"I shall keep my vest on . . . It's a warm night, though . . . Can't we have some air . . . ?"

"Careful about the blinds."

"Oh, yes. This damn black-out. We've got to get used to it again . . . That was a very good meal they gave us. Splendidly cooked . . My first acquaintance with the A.T.S. They can have my testimonial any time. They're good girls . . Who's going to put out the light?"

"Last man in bed," said the Gunner Captain, who was already there.

"Nearest to the switch," amended the Anti-Tank Gunner. "That's you, Major," he addressed the dark, silent infantryman.

At that moment a bugle in the distance blew "Lights Out." With the heavy humour characteristic of taciturn men, the Infantry Major, almost before the last strains of the call died away, plunged the room into darkness.

"By God . . . How regimental . . ." laughed the Anti-Tank Major. "Thanks, Major. You really have brought back a whiff of the good old times."

The Gunner Captain, stretching himself out luxuriously between the blankets, silently echoed the same sentiment. After the chaos of the past few weeks it was grand to feel oneself enveloped once again in all this comfortable routine of a military depôt. He had never appreciated it so keenly before. It seemed like a shield between oneself and danger. And this unusual absence of danger was exciting, too, in its own way. So was the smell of fresh-cut grass, wafted in through the open window . . . All too good to lose by going to sleep at once.

The Anti-Tank Major was addressing a few more bedtime reflections to the room in general.

"Nice old boy, the Colonel," he said. "One of the best . . . I hope he didn't consider me impolite at dinner. Several times he addressed me, and I never answered. To tell the truth, I was far too damn busy feeding to stop to talk. I was ravenous . . . Couldn't help it if it had been the King of England himself . . . All I'd had in the last forty-eight hours were four biscuits and a cup of tea . . ."

"Eating is a disgusting spectacle when a man is really in need of his food," said the R.A.M.C. Major, with the usual giggle. " I thought so when I was looking round the Mess this evening. We resembled a lot of savages . . . I don't think the Colonel minded. He's a wise old bird. He understands . . ."

Gradually the fragments of talk dwindled away and died into complete silence as the men dropped off to sleep. The Gunner Captain, before closing his eyes, glanced at the bed opposite. The fair-haired Major still sat motionless on the edge in the darkness, clothed in his battle-dress.

" Aren't you turning in, Major ? " he asked, softly.

The query seemed to jerk the Major out of a dream, though his eyes were wide open.

" Yes, I suppose I'd better," he muttered, and bent down to unfasten his boots.

*   *   *   *   *

In the middle of the night the Gunner Captain woke with a start. For the moment he could not recollect where he was. He had been dreaming of his Battery in action with the rearguard outside Dunkirk during the last stages of the Retreat. But it was not these excitements that had broken his slumbers. He had heard a real voice. A voice very close to him that seemed to be every now and then issuing orders to men in a subdued but very penetrating undertone. The room, blacked-out by the close-fitting blinds, was in complete darkness. But after a while the Gunner Captain could perceive the figure of the fair-haired Major, lying on the outside of the bed opposite, still dressed except for his boots. The figure tossed about uneasily in its sleep, mumbled something unintelligible, was silent, then, suddenly, in the penetrating undertone exclaimed :

" Mr. Hartley, who is left of your platoon ? " A

238

pause and then : " God Almighty . . . Only six.
We won't have a man left if we can't stop those
machine-guns . . . What's happened to that damned
tank rifle . . . ? "

The Gunner Captain sat bolt upright in bed, spellbound by the grim monologue. There was a pause,
some more mumbling, then the tossing man spoke
again.

" More grenades . . . More grenades . . . Be
quick, damn you . . . They're coming again . . .
Hold on, now . . . Hold on . . . We must stick
it . . ."

Another brief spell of silence, during which the
man who was fighting his battles over again turned
and tossed about in the bed more than ever.

Suddenly, as if he were addressing a friend at his
elbow, he said in a tone of pathos :

" Charles, if you come out of this alive, and I don't,
I wish you'd go along and see my wife and tell her
I love her . . ."

Almost immediately the voice changed and rang
out through the room, firm and vibrant :

" Steady, lads . . . steady . . . Here they
come . . . Here they are . . . Keep cool . . .
You're all right . . Look at 'em . . . Masses of
'em, shoulder to shoulder . . . Steady, now . . .
You can't miss . . . Give 'em another fifty yards
. . . Now then . . . Fire . . . Fire . . ."

And as, in his nightmare, he ordered volley after
volley of rifle fire, he leaped out of bed with a shout
that was half a cheer.

By this time the other occupants of the room were
thoroughly aroused, and other voices mingled with
that of the fair-haired Major.

" What the hell's all this row . . . ? "

" Who's out of bed . . . ? "

" Turn on the light, somebody . . ."

The dark, gloomy Major jumped out of bed and pressed the switch. Even as he did so a couple of revolver shots rang out, and a couple of bullets smacked the wall just above the Gunner Captain's head. The light disclosed the fair-haired Major standing in the centre of the room, revolver in hand, staring wildly about him with dazed, wide eyes. The R.A.M.C. Major, who was nearest, sprang forward and gripped the wrist that held the revolver. All the others hastened forward to assist.

But there was no struggle. The light restored to the fair-haired Major consciousness of his whereabouts. The dazed look faded from his eyes. He drew his hand across his forehead as though to brush away some lingering remnants of a dreadful vision. Then, with a half-sob, he lurched forward and fell face downward heavily on his bed.

The doctor Major sat by him uttering soothing words and winking over his shoulder at the others. After a few minutes he returned to his corner of the room and rummaged about in his haversack.

" Now you swallow these, old fellow," he said to the broken man, handing him three white tablets and a glass of water. " To-morrow you'll be as right as a trivet."

The fair-haired Major swallowed them as obediently as a child, and very soon sank into a heavy slumber.

" That'll keep him quiet for a bit," said the doctor. " But I'll take care of his gun, in case. His nerves have gone pretty bad, but he'll be all right. A few nightmares now and again, I expect. Damn nuisance, waking us all up like that."

" I don't see why, because a man has a nightmare, he should disturb the whole room," grumbled the dark, gloomy Major. " Other people don't . . ."

The four of them looked at one another a trifle self-consciously, as if the speaker had revealed a secret each preferred to conceal.

" Well, put the light out and let's get to sleep again," said the Anti-Tank Major.

The light was extinguished. The four men returned to their beds. And to their own nightmares . . .

ACTIVE SERVICE

The tall young infantry captain, clad in a British Warm, paused for a moment at the entrance to the long hospital corridor, with its pale-green shiny painted walls broken at regular intervals by chocolate-brown doors, each exactly like the other.

" One of those dreary doors is all that divides me from my fate," he reflected, in a passing flicker of despondency.

He had just arrived from London at the drab-looking hospital attached to a former cavalry barracks in an Eastern Counties town. His errand was such as to render him acutely alive to impressions, even from bricks and mortar, and the colours of doors ; though in general he was no more impressionable than most people.

He opened a door marked : " Enquiries." A nurse seated at a desk glanced up as he entered.

" I have an appointment at 2 p.m. for a Medical Board," said the young officer. " My name is Withers."

The nurse consulted her diary of appointments. " Yes. That's quite correct," she replied with a condescending smile, as though to relieve his mind from any apprehension of having committed some foolish mistake. " Will you come this way ? "

The Captain followed her along the pale-green
corridor till she opened another chocolate door,
ushered him through, and asked him to wait.   He
found himself alone in a small, lofty room with bare
walls and a window whose sill was so high from the
floor that it was impossible to look out.   The bright
sunshine filtered through the dirty panes, subdued
and misty.   In one corner of the room stood a camp-
bed with three folded grey army blankets.   A desk
occupied the centre, the only other piece of furniture
being a cumbersome old-fashioned red leather arm-
chair.   This was so decrepit that the leather in places
was crumbling into powder.   The Captain perched
himself on the arm of this chair, and the red dust
clung to the tails of his British Warm like particles
of dried blood.

Ten minutes passed.   No one came, except an
orderly who walked in, took a paper off the desk,
and walked out again without a word.   The silence
was complete, but for the spasmodic gurgling of water
in the hot-water pipes.   An irritating monologue in
the Captain's present mood, and one he could cheerfully have dispensed with.

Another quarter of an hour passed.   He began to
feel he had been forgotten.   His impatience grew.   He
wanted his business settled quickly ; to know where
he stood . . .   Confound these Medical Boards.   They
were always the same.   Never punctual.   Never in a
hurry to put a man out of his suspense.   It didn't
matter a damn to them.   They were case-hardened
. . .   Hanging about like this made a fellow begin
to dread the worst.   He had felt pretty confident
about the result during the journey from London.
But now . . .

He wrenched himself away from the black thought.
It was impossible that anything very serious could

be wrong with him . . . He had been taken ill on
leave, two months after his return from Dunkirk.
His own doctor had told him that after a couple of
months' treatment he would be as fit as ever. Before
this could begin it was necessary to have his Medical
Board. He was anxious to start the treatment without delay. The sooner he did so, the sooner he would
rejoin his regiment. He begrudged every minute they
kept him waiting. Besides, sitting alone in the dreary
room with no other distraction than the sound of
asthmatic water-pipes, engendered unpleasant fancies.
Suppose the Board did not go the right way . . .

He took another look at his watch. Half-past
two. Already they were half-an-hour overdue. Had
that nurse made any mistake about announcing
him . . .

Just as he made up his mind to go and inquire,
the door opened and a brisk young R.A.M.C. Lieutenant entered.

" You're Captain Withers, aren't you ? " he said.
" Sorry we are so late. But we can't find the third
member of the Board."

(All Medical Boards must have three or more
members.)

" He's probably consuming a second glass of port
. . . or forgotten all about it," the Lieutenant continued, rather inclined to find more humour in the
situation than did the impatient Captain.

Picking up the telephone on the desk he asked to
be put through to the Mess.

" That you, Williams ? . . . Stevenson speaking
. . . I say, old chap, is M—— over there ? . . .
What ? . . . Oh, all right . . . I say, what an
idiot old George was to play that ten of diamonds.
If it hadn't been for that we should have galloped
home. That second call of his, too. Very bad bridge.

He must have known we didn't stand an earthly.
All I had was the knave and a deuce. What could
I do with that ? . . ."

A considerable inquest on the previous night's
bridge ensued while the Captain shifted about rest-
lessly on the arm of the leather chair in his impatience,
rubbing more and more red powder on to his British
Warm.

At last the Lieutenant relinquished the 'phone.

" The chap's gone out. Nobody seems to know
where," he announced. " I'll have to go and find
somebody else."

" My fate may be of considerable importance to
me," thought the Captain ruefully, when he found
himself alone again, " but it doesn't matter a damn
to these people. That's the cold truth. I've got to
be philosophical about this. After all, I'm just
another job for them . . ."

His enforced philosophy helped him through another
long quarter of an hour. Then the Lieutenant reappeared.

" It's all right now," he said. " So long as you
don't mind a lady doctor."

The Captain would have snatched at the offer of
a chimpanzee doctor, so eager was he to get proceedings started. He followed the R.A.M.C. Lieutenant into the corridor and through another chocolate
door into a room very similar to the one he had left,
except that it contained a book-case on the wall and
a grate with a small coal-fire burning. At the desk
sat another R.A.M.C. Lieutenant, a dark, broad-
shouldered, long-faced man who wore glasses. Evidently the principal member of the Board. Behind
him stood the third member, the lady doctor who
had been roped-in at the last moment, a young woman,
not more than twenty-three years old, dressed in

248

khaki uniform with a single pip on her shoulder, and the badges of the R.A.M.C. on the lapels of her coat. The Captain took a swift, and rather shy look at her, and decided that though she possessed no pretensions to being pretty, she had some nice wavy brown hair, and a sensitive face. From her neck hung a stethoscope.

" Do sit down. I'm sorry you've been kept waiting. What's been the matter with you ? You're on leave, aren't you ? "

The man at the table hurried through the preamble as if desirous of making up for lost time. Then he reached for an Army Form and got down to business. " Name . . . Age . . . Regiment . . . Period of service . . . Foreign service . . . Date when first ill . . ." and so on till the form was filled with the answers.

" Now strip to the waist, please."

The Captain obeyed, and in turn the three doctors examined him. Each went through exactly the same routine, listening here, tapping there, prodding and knocking at his chest and back. The lady doctor was the last to officiate, and the Captain shivered slightly when she touched him. Her hands were so cold. The men's hands had been warm and moist.

" She should have a tolerably warm heart," thought the Captain, remembering the old saying.

Eventually the triple examination came to an end. The Captain re-dressed and returned to the waiting-room while the Medical Board considered its verdict. Once more he sat on the arm of the chair listening to the gurgling of the hot-water pipes. Once more the long minutes dragged out. . . . He wondered whether he would have to wait another half-hour. . . . Would it be a good sign or a bad if they sent for him quickly ? . . . He hoped that lady doctor knew her job. That she wouldn't make a fuss over something that really

didn't matter, and start magnifying trifles. . . . Still,
it would be two to one against her if she did. And
that was a majority in his favour. . . . How cold her
hands were. He fancied he could still feel his flesh
chilled where she had touched him. . . . Altogether,
he felt more confident now the examination was over.
It was all that confounded hanging about that had
brought doubts into his mind. Yes, he felt sure
he had nothing to fear. . . . Certainly not the big
thing. . . .

In five minutes he was summoned back to the
Medical Board. The three doctors occupied the same
positions as before. The young woman in khaki again
stood behind the long-faced Lieutenant at the desk,
her stethoscope dangling from her neck. It was at
her face that the Captain glanced the instant he
entered the room, striving to read in it some clue to
his fate. But a very professional blank confronted
him. He turned to the faces of the two men. On
these, also, nothing was written that could be read.

Much to the Captain's surprise, and disappointment,
no reference was made to his physical condition. The
long-faced Lieutenant simply handed him a sick-leave
pass, and told him to remain at home till he received
further orders. The War Office would communicate
the result of the Medical Board to him.

The Captain stood glancing from one to the other
of the three doctors, fingering his pass. He dared
not leave that room without knowing more. He hesitated, suddenly finding himself driven into a mood of
entreaty that made him blush and feel self-conscious.

" Can't you give me a hint of what is likely to
happen ? " he asked.

The man at the desk stretched his broad shoulders
and rose to his feet. He removed his spectacles,
wiped them, and replaced them carefully.

" Unofficially, old boy," he said, " if I were you I should get out my civilian clothes and give them a brush. You won't be in the Army much longer."

Dead silence descended on the room. The Captain swallowed a lump that rose in his throat, half choking him. His beseeching gaze travelled from one face to the other, mutely begging for some amelioration of the sentence. His distress was so evident that, for a fleeting second, a look of compassion appeared on the lady doctor's countenance.

" Isn't there . . . isn't there anything . . ." mumbled the Captain.

" Nothing . . . nothing at all," replied the long-faced Lieutenant decisively.

Between the three doctors and the Captain on the other side of the desk the distance seemed to widen. In the new chaos of his thoughts there was no help to be expected from them. Even their faces looked remote. After a few moments the Captain pulled himself together with a jerk, bade them " good after-noon," and walked out of the hospital to his waiting car.

It was an ugly journey home. Bitter thoughts occupied him. He felt bitter towards everything, beginning with the doctor who had forgotten to turn up for the Board, and ending with himself. His career, his life's ambition had been destroyed in one sentence. In that room a man had stood amid the ruins of his dearest hopes. And nobody had cared a damn. . . . How utterly lacking in the slightest sympathy or understanding the Board had exhibited itself . . . How callous, inhuman, cold . . . cold as the hands of the lady doctor. . . . Years and years of work all gone for nothing . . . Years of good com-radeship smashed in a second. . . . The regiment, in which he took so much pride, now a thing of the past. . . . All the links forged during those perilous days

of the Retreat, now broken. . . . The regiment would
march on.   But he would be left behind. . . . And
that Medical Board saw nothing more in all this than
a man " getting out his civilian clothes and giving
them a brush." . . . The brutal candour of it sickened
him.

While in the waiting-room at the hospital the
Captain had flattered himself that even if the worst
happened he could " take it on the chin."   But when
the blow fell it did not seem to land on the chin.   It
hit him somewhere in the pit of the stomach, knocking
his world about his ears, leaving him dazed, shipwrecked
without a raft.   He turned on himself with bitterness,
without pity, accusing himself for his breakdown in
health as though he had committed a crime.

" I'm a ghastly failure," he told himself.   " I've
made a complete mess of my job.   That's how people
will regard me.   And they'll be right."

Bitterest reflection of all was that if this illness
had not befallen him, instead of brushing up his
civilian clothes, he would be going up for his majority.
. . . Once more the incredibility of the disaster
stunned him.

A letter from a brother officer awaited him on his
arrival home.

" Did you see that you were mentioned in despatches
in the *Gazette* of the 15th ? " wrote his old comrade.
" So was I.   But you deserved it."

The cruel irony of it stung him to further depths of
misery.   Had he heard he had been awarded a V.C.
it would have made little difference now.   As a beginning a "mention" was something to be pleased
about.   But as an end, what did it matter ?   And
this was the end. . . .

He pitched the letter on to the table with a great
desire to blot the news entirely out of his mind.

Before going to bed that night, in grim determination to drain to the dregs his bitter dose of medicine, he opened his wardrobe and inspected his civilian suits for the first time since war broke out. He did not go so far as to brush them, but he took one out, looked it over, and tried to picture himself wearing it again. Then in a sudden fit of disgust at himself and everything, he flung it down on a chair by his bedside.

*　　　*　　　*　　　*　　　*

At midnight he was awakened by a terrific explosion that rocked the house and bounced him in his bed. For a moment he fancied he was back at Dunkirk. That bang, he knew, was a bomb, and a big one. Now he could hear the guns of London putting up a heavy barrage, and more bombs dropping, some near and some distant. A big raid was on.

Another huge explosion shook the house. " That's a near one," thought the Captain, and he began to dress hurriedly with the intention of going out and offering his assistance in the work of rescue. It wasn't till he was fastening his braces that he discovered that in his hurry he had slipped into his civilian trousers. He gave it only a passing thought, donned the waist-coat and jacket, jammed on his tin hat, grabbed his torch and ran out into the night.

He had not far to go. A hundred yards away a large bomb had fallen in a short cul-de-sac of semi-detached villas. A policeman and a group of A.R.P. workers were dragging injured men, women, and children from the ruins. An ambulance stole past him and came to a halt. Stretcher-bearers appeared. There was a strong smell of escaping gas. Amid the groaning of the injured he could hear a child crying.

In the darkness the Captain stumbled over piles of

broken brick and masonry, and shattered glass towards three shadowy figures who were frantically tugging away to shift the trunk of a tree that had sliced a house in half when it fell, and imprisoned the residents.

" Can I be of any help ? " he inquired.

" Report to that man in the white hat over there," was the reply.

The Captain clambered across more debris and offered his services to the head of the A.R.P. squad, whose tin hat was painted white.

" Yes, help me get this woman out," said the latter. " She may be alive."

The woman, elderly and grey-haired, still lay on her bed clad in a nightdress. The bed-clothes had disappeared. The bed itself had dropped through the ceiling from the first floor to the ground, and lumps of the roof and walls crushed it beneath their weight. A heavy beam lay across the woman's breast, pinning her down. No sound or movement came from her.

The Captain and the man in the white hat commenced their work. In a quarter of an hour they had extricated the woman. She was dead.

But the Captain had come to life again. During this rescue work in the black night, with the German raiders humming overhead, bombs dropping, and the crash of the barrage reverberating through the sky, a change took place in him, that, to begin with, he scarcely realised. The paralysing bitterness that had held possession of him ever since he left the hospital seemed to vanish. He was no longer conscious of the crushing weight of despondency under which he had regarded himself as finished. He had believed it was the end of everything. But now he was not so sure. . . .

A new set of thoughts took shape in his mind as,

beneath the German bombers, he worked side by side with the man in the white hat. Was not this the battlefield, here in these London streets, as truly as it had been in the fields of France and Flanders ? Were not these devoted A.R.P. workers all members of an army comparable in spirit and devotion to the one he must shortly quit for ever ? What difference did it make that they wore civilian clothes, that they were civilians ? What did the uniform or the rank matter ? After all, it was the job that counted. And these men were getting on with the big job. And he with them. . . . No, he had not come to the end. Only to another beginning. . . .

He wasn't foolish enough to imagine that he would cease to regret his broken career. He would regret that till his dying day. There would be bad moments. But at any rate, while this war lasted he had his place. . . .

THE END